A Veterinary Surgeon's Guide to

DOGS

A Veterinary Surgeon's Guide to

DOGS

David Coffey

B.Vet.Med.M.R.C.V.S.

World's Work Ltd

Text and diagrams copyright © 1980 by David Coffey
Photographs copyright © 1980 by Derek Butler
Index compiled by R. C. Raper, B.Sc., D.T.A.
Published by World's Work Ltd, Kingswood, Tadworth, Surrey
Made and printed in Great Britain by
Fakenham Press Limited, Fakenham, Norfolk
SBN 437 02500 4

Acknowledgements

My grateful thanks for help with photographic subjects are due to the following:

Mr D. Butler (page 10)

Miss E. Lane (pages 8–9 and 23)

Mrs A. M. Letheby (page 13)

Mrs F. Spector (page 27)

Mr and Mrs M. Grundy and their sons Lance and Piers (pages 40 and 69)

Mrs P. Richards (pages 58–9)

Mr and Mrs P. A. Greenwood (pages 80 and 84)

Mrs E. Geddes (pages 100 and 148)

Master D. Hudson (pages 119, 179 and 186)

Mr M. Gilbert (page 189)

Contents

Part Three

Part Four

Introduction

In recent years there has been an insidious attempt to discredit the dog's position and function in modern society. With an armoury of veiled threats, oblique legislation and intimated dangers of disease this dedicated anti-dog lobby has made and is continuing to make full use of the media to pursue its ill conceived and bigoted campaign.

Contrary to what they preach, even before man emerged from his primitive hunter-gatherer existence the relationship between man and dog was well established. Since then in spite of the growing complexity of human society the dog has been at man's side. From its early task as a hunting assistant the dog's role changed first to farming aid – shepherding and guarding the herds and flocks – and property guard, to sporting companion until finally assuming what to date is perhaps its most arduous task, vivisection exempted, as household pet. Because of its persistence and its character this unique relationship is both fascinating and exciting.

The expectation for this book is ambitious. Its function twofold. Its first task is practical, even mundane. It deals with the mechanics of dog owning – the nuts and bolts of the subject. It explains the routine management of the dog. How it is fed, housed, exercised and groomed together with detailed information on purchasing and rearing a puppy and how it should be trained. It includes practical advice on breeding, and all other aspects of canine sexuality. The section on disease is not intended to replace the function of the local veterinary surgeon but simply to recapitulate what is said during a consultation and hopefully even to explain more fully the discussion which is, because of the limitations of time, sometimes rather too brief. Where appropriate this will take the form of questions and answers – the questions being those which experience has shown are commonly posed, and therefore frequently of concern to dog owners.

The second and equally important purpose of the book is to place the domestic dog in perspective. To do this a wide range of subjects will be discussed from the evolution of the dog from primitive carnivores with a consideration of the natural history and natural behaviour of the dog's ancestors to the function and difficulties of the dog in modern society. If the very real threat by those who would happily increase the plasticated sterility of our modern society by phasing out the domestic dog is to be frustrated then a dog-owning public conversant with all aspects of the canine world is not only desirable but essential.

Part One

Evolution of the dog

Two hundred million years ago, long before the dinosaurs died out, mammals had already appeared on earth. Throughout the long reign of the dinosaurs, mammals were destined to remain small rather insignificant creatures living nocturnal lives deep in forests.

When the dinosaurs became extinct, rather suddenly in evolutionary terms, 70 million years ago, the way was left open for mammals to develop to fill the ecological gaps left by the great demise.

During the epoch known as the Palaeocene, carnivores evolved to form five main groups including what appeared to be the relatively unimportant long bodied, tree-living mammals – the Miacids – which had descended in turn from primitive insect eaters. These were destined to give rise to modern carnivores and were therefore early ancestors of our modern dogs. All primitive groups of carnivores with the exception of the Miacids were to become extinct in the Oligocene. During the Eocene some 35 million years ago development of the Miacids was slow but during this epoch they divided into two main branches one of which was to give rise to modern cats and the other to the dog and its relatives.

During the Oligocene the evolutionary direction of the dog became clearer. Developing from the primitive Miacid group, they continued as rather long bodied animals with short legs not unlike the weasels and polecats alive to-day. Mesocyon, thought to be a direct ancestral relative of the modern dog, was such a creature and lived in North America. Our modern genus of dogs – Canis – evolved in Europe during the Pliocene, spread rapidly to Africa and Asia and reached the new world in the early Pleistocene.

While modern cats developed to become lone territory loving hunters who waited hidden from their prey ready to pounce and use their short sharp canines to sever the main blood vessels of the neck, the various wild dogs including wolves were to develop a complex social structure with a rigid hierarchy. Small groups or packs co-operated to hunt the new forms of herbivores which were evolving.

The technique used by wolf and dog packs when tackling large

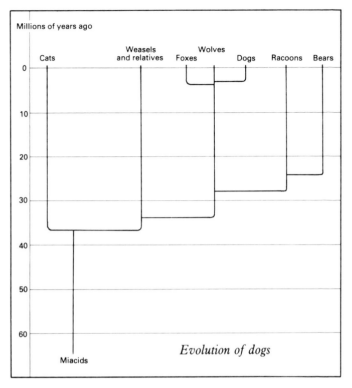

Millions of years ago

Evolution of dogs

herbivores is to single out a member of the herd – often a weak or old animal – and then to pursue it relentlessly until it tires. It is then attacked by the dogs who tear the animal to pieces. In spite of the horror we may feel this system is efficient and has great survival value. It requires considerable social communication between individual members of the pack and a high degree of co-operation.

The formation of packs, and the individual members' subservience to pack discipline, was important not only for the survival of dogs throughout prehistory but was also an essential factor for the establishment of their unique relationship with man.

Behaviour of wild dogs and wolves

To fully understand the domestic dog it is essential to study the behaviour and natural history of its ancestral species, the wolf, still found in Canada and parts of the U.S.A. Wolves have evolved over millions of years as hunters of herbivorous animals on the open plains. Small groups or packs of wolves co-operate. They single out their prey then pursue it, taking it in turns to lead the chase, countering its every twist until it tires, can be held, and torn to pieces. This way of life requires close co-operation between individuals. It requires a complex social structure within the pack. It is this social interdependence which gives the wolf and its close cousin the domestic dog their unique qualities.

The wolf pack is composed of a number of related animals. There are usually one or two pairs of breeding adults together with the survivors of previous litters. There may also be non-breeding adults present. The size of the pack is partially determined by the number of animals which can be fed from a kill. If too many animals were to be present at the kill, the food could either be shared equally, in which case none of the wolves would have sufficient or some would have a sufficiency while others would starve. It is believed that when a pack begins to enlarge to a size that threatens the survival of the members it breaks into smaller units. This over-simplifies the situation but field studies suggest that relationships between neighbouring packs of wolves depend on previous knowledge of each other. If the packs are composed of related animals which have split because of the dictates of hunting necessity, then they may greet each other with obvious signs of enthusiasm. If the packs are unrelated, there may be fighting. In addition field observations suggest there may be movement and interchange between packs. The pack, the basic unit of wolf sociology cannot be considered in isolation but only as part of a rather loosely organised area population. Indeed at certain times of the year several packs may unite for periods while small groups may leave the pack to hunt or travel separately for several days. Packs may number as few as five or six members and are rarely larger than fifteen. Occasionally individuals are seen alone.

Each pack hunts a territory. This may extend for tens or hundreds of square miles, and will probably be shared partially or completely with other packs.

Wolf packs within these territories monitor each other's movements using smell. It is reasonably certain that the dog's acute sense of smell enables it to distinguish individuals by their scent. While patrolling their territory members of the pack will check what must be to them the obvious marking places. They smell and then mark with urine. The dominant wolves go first to be followed slavishly by other members of the pack. It has been suggested that wolves can not only tell which animals were there last but how long ago. By constantly smelling these spots they build up a picture of wolf movements in the area. It is believed that if smell indicates the presence of another pack ahead, the following pack may well alter its course to avoid it. This would prevent two packs hunting the same area.

The author's pack.

Faeces too are individually scented. When a dog passes faeces some of the secretion from the anal sacs (see Part III, Anal sacs and anal glands), is expressed along the ducts which open at the anus and onto the stool. It is for this reason – communication – that dogs indulge in, what is to us, a superficially distasteful habit of smelling each other's faeces. It also explains why dogs smell each other's anal areas when they meet.

The large hunting territories are not defended. No attempt is made to reject other wolves from the territory. Aggressive encounters would only occur if the two packs met and were not known to each other or if there were established antagonism between them. The home or den area is another story. An area is selected by the pack and a den or dens dug and prepared in which the pregnant females can have their young. This is vigorously defended against other wolves. The cubs are born underground and stay there until a few weeks old when they begin to venture from the den to play. At this time the non-breeding adults go out to hunt, leaving the breeding females to look after the cubs. When the adults return to the den area after a successful hunt the nursing females lick the faces and mouths of the returning hunters which stimulates them to regurgitate food from their stomach. This the females rapidly consume. An incredible degree of social co-operation! As the pups grow the mother may herself join in the hunt leaving her cubs in the den. On her return the pups go through a similar face and mouth licking behaviour inducing her to regurgitate food for them. Indeed pups will approach all members of the pack, not just their mother. All members of the pack then accept responsibility for rearing the pups.

Within each pack, life depends on a system of social dominance. Discipline is essential for survival. This is not a rigid linear pack order, often described for chickens, in which animal A dominates all below it while animal B dominates all but A and so on. Indeed such a simple system does not in reality exist in chickens. Each pack will have socially senior animals and probably a single pack leader. Among the male wolves each will know and largely respect its relationship with all other wolves. Some will be dominant others more subservient. The order is not so rigid and inflexible as to be unchangeable. Its structure depends on age as well as on individual personality. Young males originally subservient will, with increasing maturity, attempt to improve their social position. Female wolves will also have an established order of dominance. Some females will be hesitant and submissive while others will appear confident. There will also be accepted relationship between males and females based both on dominance and sexual behaviour. Dominant males and females usually enjoy a close easy relationship – indeed wolves are believed to pair for life. Individuals within a pack appear to have preferences for other individuals; they appear to have special 'friends'.

Young cubs enjoy the status of their mother. If she is a dominant female they will be protected from the other adults. If she is subservient they may well have a harder time. Cubs have their own dominance orders within the litter. As they mature the influence of their mother lessens and they are forced to establish their own relationships within the pack.

We have seen how smell is used by dogs for territorial communication between packs. Communication within the pack or for close encounters between different packs depends, in addition, on visual and vocal signs. Precise information can be gleaned about a wolf's mood, emotional state and intentions by observing its stance, posture, facial expression, position of lips, placing of the ears and tail elevation. Vocal communication, almost certainly used to keep members of the pack in touch when they are out of each other's sight, can also be used to intensify aggression and to support postural body language in intimate exchanges between individuals.

It is to be hoped that this necessarily brief and simplified discourse will help us to understand more fully the sociology of the wolf and to appreciate the complex social behaviour of the domestic dog. Hopefully those interested in the natural history and behaviour of the dog will be stimulated to study the wolf for a deeper insight into the mentality of the dog.

Domestication

All the available scientific evidence suggests that the dog's ancestor is the wolf – the domestic dog is a wolf in fancy dress. Exactly how the dog became domesticated some ten thousand years ago remains a mystery but an understanding of man's life style at the time together with a knowledge of the wolf's behaviour allows us to speculate with some anticipation of accuracy. One must imagine primitive men living in small family groups or tribes hunting wild animals and supplementing the spasmodic supply of fresh meat with roots, berries and other fruits in season. The camps of these men would be primitive, often temporary, but at night they would have a fire. To these camp sites, we must imagine, came such small packs of wolves attracted either by the fire or more likely scavenging offal and scraps, left-overs from the men's kill.

At first the men would have kept the wolves at bay with a bombardment of rocks. Over a period of time, perhaps several generations, a loose relationship may have grown between local tribes and their wolf neighbours. Mutual acceptance even respect may have allowed the relationship to develop. Familiarity may have assisted the

Yorkshire terrier and great dane, but which dominates?

formation of a bond. The presence of wolves surrounding the camp at night may have proved useful in preventing unwelcome attentions of the other animals and they may well have acted as a warning of trouble if not actually guarding the camp. Some of the bolder wolf packs may have accompanied the men on hunting expeditions, no doubt keeping their distance, but one must imagine that as a quarry was sighted or found in a prepared trap, excitement among both men and wolves would have increased and overcoming their fear of the men the wolves would rush in to deal with the unfortunate victim. Man, ever the opportunist, would have encouraged such participation since it left the dangerous job of dealing death to the large and formidable prey to the wolves. Once the animal was killed the men would have driven off the wolves and kept the kill for themselves allowing the wolves only the less palatable parts as a reward.

William the labrador retriever and Lucy watch television.

No doubt the relationship was further enhanced if when a wolf mother was killed puppies were taken by children as pets. We know from experience with modern wolf cubs that if reared in close proximity to man the animals would have developed precisely the kind of bond puppies do with man to-day. Primitive man would have no doubt noted the enhanced value of such animals, they being more amenable to his bidding than their wild relatives, and would have reared and bred from this 'domesticated' stock. The story of the domestic dog had begun.

Behaviour of domestic dogs

An overwhelming weight of evidence from many species, besides the dogs, confirms that domestication has virtually no effect on behaviour. It seems much easier to alter the physical characteristics of a species than change its psychology. Dogs are therefore simply wolves in fancy dress. This basic premise is essential to a complete understanding of the dog. Evidence in support of the hypothesis that dogs descend from wolves comes from many scientific disciplines, but perhaps two examples will serve to illustrate. A research worker in America allowed a mixed group of dogs of various breeds their free-dom in a very large enclosure away from human interference. Observers reported that after a short period of adjustment the behaviour of these dogs and certainly that of their puppies was indistinguishable from that of wolves. Further, a personal communication from an American veterinary surgeon who is concerned with the rehabilitation of captive wolves to the wild, confirmed that domestic dogs can and have established themselves harmoniously in captive wolf packs, both dog and wolf behaving identically.

The unique quality of dogs is their ability to accept man and the human family as their pack – substitute sociology. Where several dogs live together their relationship and responses to each other will closely parallel their ancestor, the wolf. Where they live isolated from other dogs or indeed with a mixture of both humans and other dogs they have the ability to adapt their behaviour. Dogs respond to us as if we are dogs. It must astound them when we do not reciprocate. Without malice they humour our demands and expectations and learn to respond to our words and gestures. They rapidly glean the gestures which please and those which win rewards. Sadly perhaps few humans bother to return the compliment and make even a superficial attempt to understand the mind of the dog.

Family dogs recognise the limits of their home area and will usually defend it against strangers who attempt to enter without permission. When out walking over what substitutes for a hunting territory they check the marking posts and deposit their own spot of liquid informa-tion. Off the lead dogs keep with their owners as wolves do with the pack. Puppies play as they would in the pack, develop as adolescent wolves do and try to assert dominance as they mature. Their patterns of feeding, drinking, exploring and elimination, are similar to those of wolves. Sexual behaviour, if allowed full expression, remains unchanged. Bitches give birth to puppies, and rear them in ways which do not alter detectably from their ancestors. Dogs like wolves need the social security of the pack. Reared with sensitivity and kept with understanding, dogs will repay their owners with loyalty and companionship.

With greater knowledge and understanding of dog and wolf behaviour many of the difficulties which arise in domestic dogs would never materialise. So very many of the problems arise from our failure to understand what is normal behaviour and to think how human existence pressurises our pet dogs.

Play

Play is an important activity for both young and old. Young animals play a great deal and in so doing gain valuable experience of their abilities both physical and mental. Play is a vital factor in preparing young mammals for adult life. It is a mistake, however, to consider play simply as a training activity for later life. Indeed its value in this connection could be seen as an almost incidental benefit. To take the simplistic view of play leads to false argument. It has been said for example by those defending the rigid management systems found in modern intensive veal production that since the calves are not to become adult, play is unnecessary. This extreme posture could not be defended if a more generous and realistic view of play is adopted. To follow such an argument to its logical conclusion one would have to hold the view that a child suffering from a disease which sadly dictated that it is to die young would not need to play. Of course such a view is stupid. Parents of such a child would ensure that it had more than adequate opportunity to play. They would appreciate the reality that play has an intrinsic value unrelated to its importance as a learning tool for the future. There appears then to be the need to engage, even indulge, in activities of a frivolous or purposeless nature as some kind of release or mechanism to buffer the individual against boredom or routine. Adults play with young of their species but also with other adults.

Play in the dog takes several forms. The commonest is the mock fight, the rough and tumble. Puppies within a litter engage in this type of play several times each day. The single puppy on its own in a family will enjoy such a game with its owners. Make sure you don't hurt the puppy but a hand pushing and rolling the puppy will substitute well for litter mates. As with all young mammal mock fights, including

Even adult dogs need to play – English setter and golden retriever.

children, this can get out of hand and turn into a demonstration of real aggression when tempers are lost. When this happens in the litter participants tend to stop the battle and move away from each other. You should do the same if the puppy shows real temper.

Puppies also play a canine modification of 'catch', tearing round over and under any obstacle, one chasing the other. Puppies do this on their own when separated from the litter. Dogs of all ages enjoy knocking or pushing a 'toy' – a bowl, ball, rubber bone etc – and then pouncing on it in mock attack. Dogs will also learn to play games which both owner and dog can enjoy together – a kind of natural play substitute. For example dogs will play hide and seek, retrieve balls or sticks and will hold a proffered object while the owner shakes it in an attempt to make the dog release its hold.

It takes little thought to appreciate the importance of play to dogs of all ages and particularly to puppies. Some breeds – the terriers for example – are more playful than others but all enjoy a game. To deny play is to deny a vital behaviour.

Understanding dogs

Some people are good with dogs, others are quite hopeless. Gifted dog owners may be born not made, but a great deal can be done by any individual who is prepared to observe without prejudice, learn with understanding and act with sensitivity.

We have seen that domestication has done little or nothing to alter the behaviour of the dog. The domestic dog, just like its ancestor the wolf, chooses to live in social groups to which it owes its absolute allegiance. Within the pack exists a well developed social hierarchy. So intense is this acceptance of social order in the dog that the behavioural need can transcend species and will be transferred to the human family with which it lives in domestication.

The dog regards itself as an integrated member of the human pack with all of the accompanying rights and responsibilities. It accepts domestication and discipline from members of the human pack to which it feels inferior but is likely to demonstrate its superior position with suitable aggression to any human pack member who it regards as a social upstart – a usurper. Social positions are not however maintained in the wolf or dog pack with persistent brutality or repeated acts of aggression; much more is the relationship based on social confidence.

Good dog owners, whether they understand the theory of dog mentality or are simply responding intuitively, assume a dog's subservience from puppyhood much as would a wolf pack leader. They never show fear of the dog because they quite simply never feel any. They indicate to the dog with patience, understanding and firmness what is expected of it and demand compliance with those wishes. Any dog with abhorrent behaviour which does not comply with routine demands of pack discipline – which is mentally abnormal – is simply not tolerated. Such a situation would surely exist in a pack of wolves or dogs. Deranged dogs and wolves would be killed. Good dog owners have the ability, intuitive or patiently learned, of reacting at the dog's level of mentality – when dealing with a dog they use the dog's standards of behaviour. They think dog.

Bad owners are commonly quite unatare of the dog's mental mechanics. From the very start of their relationship with a puppy they are anxious, some are frankly frightened. I recall one owner presenting an eight-week-old puppy for its first vaccination. Before holding it for the injection he put on a pair of thick gardening gloves. I suggested these were superfluous to requirement for any dog let alone an eight-week-old puppy. I spent a little time explaining the rudiments of dog behaviour and the basics of training. The puppy needless to say was a perfectly normal animal, simply full of fun, a little free and generous, as are all puppies, with its needle-sharp teeth. Four weeks later when the owner returned with the puppy for its second injection out came the gloves again. It was apparent that the situation was rapidly deteriorating. The owner was now positively ill at ease when handling the pup. Eight months later the dog, now completely out of control, was put down following a savage attack on a young child.

We have seen how, in the dog or wolf pack, the puppy is dependent upon its mother for protection and social status. It is not subjected to the hierarchical discipline and constrictions of the adult members of the pack. Adult members will often play with a puppy as will its mother. The response of a mother to an aggressive act against her puppy will be protective but will also be influenced by her own social position. Dominant bitches will administer quite severe corrective measures to any member of the pack which attacks or chastises her puppies. Submissive, low cast bitches may well be forced to accept the situation with little attempt at retaliation.

As a puppy matures it will be forced to adopt a social position among the adults, forced to find its place in the pack. Dominance orders are by no means rigid, or inviolate. As young dogs mature they will try to improve their social position and status. Old dogs will be toppled from power by younger, stronger animals.

The fluctuating nature of dominance orders in the pack should be remembered by owners particularly as a puppy matures to adulthood. As it grows the young adult will be more difficult to control; it may well begin to challenge for status. In my experience such a challenge is much more likely from the male dog than the bitch. Providing the human pack leader has maintained dominance throughout adolescence to maturity the adult dog usually settles to its position and outbursts of indiscipline become rare.

So important to the dog is its social relationship with its pack that I believe an understanding of it, whether instinctive or learned, is crucial to an understanding of dog behaviour; a consideration is essential if a puppy is to mature into a well-adjusted member of a human pack.

Hierarchy – the dominance order – is the basic mechanics of social behaviour in the dog. It would be wrong to imply that to understand their function is to understand dogs. Like the social behaviour of any of the higher mammals, life in a pack is complex and full of subtlety. Pack leaders may be good, responsible and able, in which case the

pack will be well integrated, peaceful and successful. They may be bad in which case there will be social strain and bickering with reduced survival efficiency.

Communication is an essential feature of social behaviour. In the wolf or dog pack this is complex. In recent years it has become fashionable to talk of body language. In reality only the name is new. The language is certainly as old as the vertebrates. Indeed for all man's feeling of superiority over the lower orders he still uses body language in everyday life. Body language is more precise and is less likely to be misinterpreted than the spoken or written word.

People who have close association with dogs learn to recognise the language of body postures and facial expressions. They can identify the moods of dogs and anticipate their intentions. Veterinary surgeons very quickly learn to interpret the mood of a patient and are only too quickly able to read the signs of aggression. Failure is rapidly rewarded with a wound.

Much of this language is difficult to teach to others because very often those skilled in its recognition have learnt it from many years of experience and are rarely conscious of the signs they see. Some of the signs are however well known. Dogs wag their tail to indicate pleasure, the hair along the back goes up to indicate aggression, snarling and baring of the molar teeth are warnings one ignores at one's peril. In addition to these well known examples there are many more subtle signs, such as narrowing of the eyes as an indication of submission, an attempt to placate. Subtle variations in the position of the ears, stance of the body, elevation of the tail, are just a very few examples of body language used to communicate the emotional state or intention of one dog to another.

In addition to body language, sounds are used by dogs in communication. These are often equally subtle but available to human beings who wish to understand the mind of the dog. We are however virtually excluded from one important sense used by dogs in social interaction – smell. Our pathetic nasal apparatus is but a shadow of the canine sense. We must accept that in our attempts to communicate with dogs we are somewhat in the position of an Englishman with but a smattering of French talking to a Sardinian philosopher.

Nevertheless for those who are prepared to accept that dogs can only be understood if we are prepared to use their methods of social behaviour and communication rich rewards can be anticipated. Those owners who attempt to elevate their dogs to sub-humanity, attributing alien stands of behaviour and consciousness to them, will not only fail

The author's youngest daughter with her constant companion Dora, a cavalier King Charles spaniel.

to reap full pleasure from their dogs' company but will do them an injustice.

Dogs and people: their social relations

Dogs adopt the human family as their pack. They make, and for over ten thousand years have made, the assumption that they are to exist in close social relationship with man. To do this they use the same, or closely similar, methods of social interaction as they would with other dogs in the pack. When being admonished they either stand in a position of submission with their ears forced back, eyes closed to slits with tails between their legs or they lie on their side with one hind leg raised to expose their vulnerable belly as they would to a dominant dog.

Greeting

When dogs greet their owners the behaviour is not dissimilar to that shown to returning members of a dog pack. They wag their tail, whine, show great excitement and leap, raising the forelegs from the ground. Some dogs will even take your arm gently in their mouth as they would a pack member's leg.

Smiling

Some dogs, not all, but some, 'smile'. They raise the front part of their lips to expose their incisor teeth. This is not as some inexperienced people assume an act of aggression or snarl, but an act of appeasement.

Licking

We have seen (See Behaviour of wild dogs and wolves) that puppies lick the face of adult members of the pack including their mothers when soliciting regurgitation of food. Face licking has developed into a method of social interaction – a sign of affection. Dogs therefore try to lick our faces to show affection and demonstrate to us the strength of our social bond with them.

To some of us, with our latter day hysteria for hygiene, this is repugnant. So be it.

Sleeping in contact

That dogs are prepared, indeed choose, to sleep in close contact with us demonstrates the intensity of the bond they feel with us. Wild dogs of the same pack sleep close together. It is not everybody who chooses to share their bed with a dog. There are several aesthetic, a few medical, but no, definitely no, behavioural arguments against the practice.

Stroking

The pleasure man and dog get from the act of stroking has at first sight no basis in normal dog behaviour. Dogs do not stroke each other. It is however not dissimilar to the nibbling one dog does to another, a kind of modified grooming with the incisor teeth. The pleasure dogs get from being stroked may be related to this behaviour. As for man, the basis of much intimate human social behaviour is based on touch. No doubt man derives the pleasure of stroking from demonstrating his close relationship with the dog.

Behavioural problems

Behavioural problems fall into two categories. That which relates to normal behaviour but which is unacceptable to the owner and that which is definitely abnormal. The former are far more common and all too often occur because of the owner's inability to understand and train dogs. While some people seem to have a natural sympathy with dogs others are less fortunate and experience considerable difficulty in attaining a harmonious relationship.

There is no real substitute for experience but a great deal can be done to prevent problems emerging. Any inexperienced owner should read as much as possible about training but should remain critical. Some dog training methods are extremely suspect. High on my list of reading material would be books on the behaviour of wolves and wild dogs. If you understand the behaviour of the ancestral and related species you will be well on the way to understanding the domestic dog. Attend obedience classes and dog shows before you get your puppy. Join a dog club, and attend any lectures they arrange. Get involved with dogs for a while. You don't have to make it a lifelong commitment. You would not buy a motor car before you have learnt to drive. Just try to read and learn about dogs.

Problems arise all too often because owners simply do not think dog. Dogs must be rewarded when they do right and punished when they do wrong. This would seem to be based on straightforward common sense and indeed it is. Problems arise because the pattern is not followed. An example may illustrate. Owners sometimes have difficulty in getting their dog to come to them. One should call the dog's name and when it arrives congratulate it and pet it. Do not try to establish this pattern when the dog is in the middle of a game, having a mad half an hour. Dogs, particularly puppies, in a high state of excitement are not receptive to any form of restriction or discipline. Choose a quiet period, the right psychological moment, and then call firmly. If the dog refuses to come do not, repeat do not, move towards it but turn and walk away or just totally ignore it. Wait a minute or so then try again. If you still do not get a positive response, speak more sharply – the punishment – be more severe in posture and attitude, then, when the puppy comes, reward with petting. In practice if you are positive in your approach, choose the right moment to impose your will and follow the reward and punishment routine, you will succeed. Punishment rarely needs to be more than a stern voice or a turn away from the dog. Normal dogs are anxious to please.

Some owners have difficulty getting their dog to come when out for walks. First point, always let the dog free in the woods or fields from the very start, as soon as the vaccination programme allows it to go out. At first it will be hesitant, a little unsure of itself and will be receptive to your commands. It will be even more anxious to please – you are the only familiar thing around. Puppies when first out do not charge over the horizon as soon as they are let off the lead. Call the pup then. It will come, pleased to experience your support and concern. Later do not expect it to come as soon as it is off the lead. Having got used to walks and the fun involved it will not be prepared to come just then. It is a bad psychological time. Wait until it has run off its first exuberance. Then when you call use a stern sharp voice perhaps patting your thigh or squatting, patting the ground. When it comes, even if not right up to you, congratulate and then walk on. It has responded positively – at least partially. If it refuses to come at all, then turn and walk away – the punishment – it will come running after you.

Many so called behavioural problems are in fact manifestations of normality. Puppies chew a wide variety of objects. They bite and chew their owners as they would litter mates. It is important to distinguish between play and that point when the puppy loses its temper and shows real aggression. When that occurs stop playing – the punishment – to show that aggression will not be tolerated. Burying bones in the flower beds may infuriate a dedicated horticulturalist but will seem perfectly normal to the dog. Bitches with false pregnancy will also dig huge holes in the garden, in preparation of a den for the puppies her body tells her are coming. People are even concerned about the frequent stops made by male dogs to sprinkle urine at every lamp post – a perfectly normal piece of behaviour.

Owners new to dog keeping must not expect dogs to behave as mechanical robots. They have a complex behavioural repertoire, individual idiosyncrasies, and a real need to express their personality. Don't have a live dog if a china ornamental facsimile would suit your purpose more efficiently.

Many behavioural problems have been dealt with under separate headings in different parts of the book. Thus house training and sexual behaviour are dealt with separately. A few problems of great concern are dealt with below. They act as examples to demonstrate the principles.

Behavioural problems can often be ameliorated by suitable treatment. The techniques are however subtle and often very time consuming. Each problem requires careful analysis, often in the home environment, to establish both the precise behaviour of the animal and the responses of the owner. A careful programme to correct the fault can then be devised, explained to owners and most important monitored throughout the period of treatment. This is expensive in time and therefore money. While dog classes are useful for training the dog to be obedient and perform certain well prescribed tasks they may have limited success with problem dogs because of the techniques they use for behavioural restructuring. When problems arise careful thought and wise application of corrective therapy may solve the problem. Unfortunately there has been little interest until recently in behavioural problems in veterinary medicine and competent advice and guidance can be difficult to obtain. Things are beginning to improve. Ask your veterinary surgeon for help or ask him to refer you to somebody who can give assistance.

Aggression

Perhaps one of the commonest causes for concern results from a dog's aggressive behaviour which is itself closely related to social dominance. Each individual within a pack has and knows its relationship with every other member. Dominance orders are a convenient method of reducing aggression within a pack, because each encounter does not have to be decided by an act of aggression, each potential combatant responding simply to the intention. It must not be imagined that dominance orders are totally rigid and inflexible. When puppies leave the protection of their mother they have to establish their own position in the pack. At first this will be rather lowly, but as they mature they will improve their status.

In the human pack, dogs must accept that their position is lowly and must so remain. Children take the dominant position afforded them by their parents – DOMINANT TO THE DOG. Problems do arise when, because of certain behavioural difficulties exhibited by the human pack, or because the dog is a dominant animal by inclination, this situation is not accepted by the dog. It has been stressed (See Part II, Male or female) that many of the difficulties are avoided if a bitch is chosen as a family pet rather than a dog, aggression being related in part to the male sex hormone. Prevention is always better than cure. If the situation is clarified for the puppy by repressing any attempt at dominance at the first sight, problems will be less likely to arise when it matures.

While many of the aggressive problems arise because the owners do not understand dogs, there are cases when dogs behave with irrational aggression. The dog for example that suddenly attacks without provocation while being fondled. Such dogs are abnormal. They cannot be tolerated. Euthanasia is the only sensible alternative in such cases. Indeed whenever aggressive patterns are established for whatever reason, it points to a failed social situation. To attempt treatment at this stage is fraught with danger. The dog should either be passed to an experienced dog owner who must be made fully aware of the problem or euthanasia should be performed. Aggressive dogs are dangerous and can inflict terrible wounds.

Chewing

Dogs of all ages have the ability and, it seems, often the desire to chew. Chewing bones and hide in the wild provides an important part of the nutritional requirements of the Canidae (Dog family). In addition chewing after the intake of large quantities of meat probably stimulates digestive juices thus aiding digestion. It also provides, for dogs and wolves, the essential period of relaxation and psychological well being after the exertions of the hunt, the uncertainties of the kill and the social difficulties of consumption – the equivalent of our coffee, port, cigars and good conversation.

Puppies go through a period of chewing anything, carpets, chairs, shoes, gloves – anything. They always seem to select expensive items, never those dispensable. How much of this is essential for dental development and how much is due to their behavioural need to explore their environment is unknown. Like children, and indeed all young mammals, they probably wish to test their environment, the things they find around them, against their well-established standard, a soft warm milk-producing mother's breast. The best method of making such a comparison is to pop whatever it is mouthwards. Since punishment of normal behaviour is unreasonable, even stupid, owners should be careful to remove valuable objects from puppies and young immature adults and should offer for attention such excellent objects as hide chews now commercially available. Needless to say excessive chewing is also a result of boredom. Puppies left alone will chew. Two puppies, or a puppy with its mother or a trustworthy adult

The confidence of a child with a large dog, resulting from a balanced relationship.

dog with whom the puppy has developed a social bond will have less time to be bored, less time to chew. Two dogs are better than one. (See Part II, One dog or two)

Eating faeces (Coprophagia)

There is no denying that this practice is to us humans a disgusting habit. A habit which tests the adoration of the most indulgent owner. If however we examine the activities of our pets' wild cousins we find this 'abnormal and disgusting habit' is part of normal behaviour.

Wild dogs and wolves will eat the faeces of herbivores (grass eating animals) upon which they prey and have also been observed to eat the faeces of members of their own pack. Closely related may be the observation that pack members will lick and clean each other's anal area. Possible explanation for these activities can be sought. Dogs and wolves may eat the faeces of herbivores to obtain roughage. (See Part III, Eating grass) The faeces of herbivorous animals also contain plentiful supplies of vitamins of the B complex. Pet dogs which consume horse and other herbivore faeces are therefore behaving normally.

The explanation for eating a dog's own faeces or that of other dogs is less obvious. Mothers consume their puppies' faeces, as part of normal maternal behaviour. Coprophagia may therefore be normal care-giving behaviour extended to the packs as a social phenomenon. Young animals need to have their intestines 'seeded' with micro-organisms from the environment after birth. Eating each other's faeces may ensure that all members of the pack have the same essential micro-organisms living in their intestines.

The sense of smell and its mechanisms in the dog remain largely a mystery to man. When a dog passes faeces, anal gland secretion is spread on the faeces. This is an essential method of communication in dogs. (See Part III, Anal sacs and anal glands) It is just possible that consumption of faeces, and therefore the anal gland secretion, stimulates the recipient's sense of smell and teaches the dog to recognise the smell again. Certainly taste and smell are closely related senses. Many dogs reaching maturity stop eating their own or other dogs' faeces. A few persist.

Whether these explanations are factual or figments of a vivid imagination they do emphasise the normality of coprophagia as a behaviour pattern and the futility of seeking a cure by adjusting diets, feeding additives or inflicting drugs.

Dogs excited in the car

Many of these problems can be overcome. It is naturally wiser to prevent them developing. From the very start get the puppy used to riding in the car. Take it for very frequent short drives – along the road and back home. Take it out for longer drives as it becomes accustomed to the car but do not always end up with something exciting like a walk in the woods. If you establish the pattern that a car ride always means fun, it will be so overcome with anticipation that excitement and crying will be inevitable. If necessary leave the dog in the car for various periods while it is stationary at home to accustom it to the environment. Even feed the dog in the car.

When a problem has developed patience and time are required to correct it. Assuming the dog becomes hysterical in the car, first get it used to a stationary car. You may sit in the car with doors open, the dog being free to enter or leave at will. While it behaves calmly talk to it soothingly. When it begins to get excited ignore it. Then close the doors with you and the dog in and repeat. Leave the dog in the car and feed it in the car. When it remains calm with the engine off start the engine. If this produces excitement stop the engine, leave the car at once, the dog remaining in it. When it calms down return start the engine. If excitement recurs stop the engine and leave until it calms again. Repeat until the dog accepts the started engine, without response. If, when you start to move in the car, the excitement begins again, stop the car and leave it. When the dog calms down return and move again. Repeat until you can travel without excitement. It is pointless to chastise the dog for excitement, it makes matters worse. (See Part II, Travelling with dogs)

Destructive dogs

All puppies chew and all puppies will cause some damage in the home. If you are not prepared to accept this don't get a puppy. Dogs which are destructive when left are a quite different problem. Dogs are social animals and do not like being left alone. Many will tolerate isolation for long periods but there are some individuals which become extremely distressed if their owners leave them. They first become agitated, begin to scratch at doors, walls, or furnishings and relieve their anxiety by tearing or chewing with dedication. The result is expensive. To hit such dogs is quite pointless. By the time you arrive home they are in a state of extreme agitation. They are so pleased to see you that no matter what you do it is better than isolation. They do not connect their destructive efforts with the corporal punishment you inflict.

It is always better to prevent this situation developing. From the start accustom the dog to being left alone for short periods. As you leave send the dog to its bed and walk away without making a fuss of it. The fussing comes when you return to a whole, undamaged, room. Gradually increase the periods of isolation. The puppy will normally accept it, if not enjoy it.

If a problem develops there are several alternatives. The simplest is not to leave the dog alone. In some cases this can be arranged. Taking the dog in the car with you is an alternative to leaving it at home alone. When this is not possible some dogs respond well simply to having the run of the house. A second dog will often stop the destructive behaviour because, of course, it is no longer alone. (See Part II, One dog or two)

Where these alternatives are not acceptable, behavioural restructuring must be attempted.

The dog should be left with a positive and stern command to stay. The owner then leaves, closing the door. Returning within a minute, the dog is fussed providing there is no damage. If there is damage the dog is ignored. Do not hit the dog for destruction. It does not help. When it is used to being left for very short periods gradually increase the period. Simple, yes, but it takes the owner nerve and considerable patience.

Digging

Dogs dig in the wild. They bury food and they dig dens in which they have their young. Pet dogs will often dig holes to bury bones for future use. Bitches will often dig enormous holes during false pregnancy. Dogs will also dig under fences to escape. Puppies often dig. Digging is difficult to stop as is any normal behaviour. Excessive punitive correction is unjustified. You can restrict the dog to areas of concrete or enclose it in a run but perhaps if you are a passionate gardener it may be wise not to have a dog.

Rolling in foul smelling rubbish and animal droppings

This is a normal, if socially unpleasant, habit. Dogs discover the perfumed prize, take a sniff then drop with their shoulder on the spot and roll. It is suggested that the scent so obtained confuses their prey and therefore assists hunting.

Development of breeds

When man first domesticated dogs and began to make use of their unique qualities to assist and ease his life it was surely natural for him to favour the offspring of those animals who demonstrated the attributes he most admired and which were of most practical use to him. Just how long it took for him to realise the advantages of selecting dogs with suitable characteristics as parents for future generations must remain a matter of speculation. One thing is certain. During the ten thousand years or so since dogs were first domesticated they have been subject to more stringent breeding techniques to produce greater diversity of breed types than any other species of animal.

Originally, breeding must have been very random. There would have been no division of labour among the dogs in the camps of primitive man. The task of all dogs would have been to defend the camp and assist hunting parties. As man changed his life style from a hunter–gatherer to pasturalist, varied canine duties would have emerged. Large dogs with a strong tendency to show aggression to strangers would have been prized as camp guards. Those with a predilection for protecting and guarding sheep and cattle from wild predators would have proved very valuable. Later, animals with ability to round up and work the flocks and herds would have been bred selectively to fix this most useful characteristic.

Two samoyeds and, in the foreground, a rare Japanese spitz, owned by breeder Mrs Spector.

As the structure of human society developed to produce an aristocratic or leisured class with time to spend in the pursuit of pleasure, dogs were selectively bred to satisfy their needs. Thus a number of types of dogs were developed for use in a variety of sports. Dogs with good eyesight and great speed were developed to pursue quarry over open ground – the sight hounds. Others were selectively bred which showed the ability to follow an animal using smell – the scent hounds. One of man's less endearing qualities has been the pleasure he derives from watching animals of one kind or another fight each other. To satisfy this bizarre need a number of strains emerged which showed courage to the point of stupidity. Dogs used for fighting bears, bulls, badgers and even each other are a living monument to man's cruelty and insensitivity. These are essentially the bull breeds and the terriers which in spite of the use for which they were bred have characteristics and qualities which endear them to man. In general man used large animals like the ox for transport and the horse for travelling. In some territories however, notably those covered with snow, breeds of dog were developed which could and would pull heavy loads over long distances.

The essential feature of early breeds of dog was function. They had to perform prescribed tasks and so long as they did so their looks were largely irrelevant. To a great extent this remains true of working dogs. Many which win acclaim for their functional ability would not be highly placed on the show bench. That types of dog, which were selected for function, resemble each other physically was an inevitable result of line and inbreeding.

The well being of those dogs man breeds for function is reasonably well protected. For if any strain or breed of working dog develops structural or temperamental faults along with the attributes for which it is prized its line will rapidly be discontinued: any working dog has to be able to do its job.

For centuries man has kept some dogs purely as pets. Their sole function to be to provide aesthetic, emotional or environmental enrichment for their owners. The Chinese began to produce a number of small breeds specifically for pets over one thousand years ago. Building on the dog's temperamental suitability for close social contact with man they dispensed with the normal facial format and selected a head shape, rounded with large eyes, now known to release parental behaviour in humans, in particular triggering mothering in woman. Chinese dog breeding produced the pekinese. A puppy from this ancient line was presented to Queen Victoria. They have been firm favourites ever since. Several centuries ago a line of diminutive spaniels were produced as pets in England. King Charles II was so fond of them that they now bear his name.

Since the industrial revolution of the last century an increasing percentage of people have been forced to live in urban areas. Some basic heritage has ensured that in spite of a reduction in the dog's functional role it remains a treasured adjunct to many human packs: dogs are still kept as pets in large numbers.

With the declining demand for dogs with a working function came a change of emphasis. Breeding became an amusing hobby indulged in more and more by those who viewed dogs as objects of aestheticism rather than as working companions. Looks became more important than their physical ability or mental astuteness. This change of direction can be regarded as a watershed of canine welfare. With the introduction of dog shows and breed societies came arbitrary breed standards. The shape of dogs was changed with no purpose in mind but human gratification. The Western world continued and intensified what the Chinese started centuries ago. Little or no thought appears to have been given to the well being of dogs so subjected. We now see the physical characteristics of some breeds exaggerated to a point so far removed from the basic canine structure that cruelty is inevitable, for example the breathing difficulties of brachycephalic (flat-faced) dogs.

In addition to the structural excesses to which dogs have been subjected, years of line and inbreeding by those with little knowledge of or responsibility for the consequences have led to a worrying increase in the burden of canine genetic disease. A great deal of time is now wasted by the veterinary profession, not to mention the misery suffered by the afflicted animals, dealing with inherited problems such as hip dysplasia which are a direct result of ill-informed breeding programmes.

This state of affairs is to be deplored. The fascinating behavioural characteristics which enabled the dog to share such a close liaison with man through thousands of years of his history have hardly been modified. An attempt should be made to rectify the current situation. We should concentrate on the behavioural facets of the dog and be far less concerned with success on the show bench. Dogs should be enjoyed for their personality not for the particular wrapping we choose for them. It is a question of balance. The selection of certain strains with a propensity for specified tasks is a fact of history. The breeding of animals to some totally arbitrary standards which can and have produced physical discomfort and predisposed certain breeds to an increased incidence of genetic disease is an abuse of man's power.

It is to be hoped that the growing concern expressed by the more enlightened breeders and others concerned with the welfare of dogs will be leading to a more rational balance between looks, function and temperament.

Dogs in modern society

In recent years there has been a dedicated anti-dog campaign by certain sections of society, which has encouraged irrational fears in the population in pursuance of its bigoted aim. What is the reality?

Keeping pet dogs is criticised from several standpoints. They are said to be dirty and carriers of disease.

Many diseases are species specific. That is to say they affect only one species and do not pass from dog to cat, cat to man, horse to cow, etc. The most dangerous animal to man is therefore another man. Those diseases that are carried by dogs and which are transmissible to man are largely under control and do not represent a social problem. In recent years there has been persistent media pressure concerning the role of worms passed from dog to man. Man has lived with dogs for thousands of years in conditions far less hygienic than we enjoy to-day. The relationship can hardly be said to have decimated man's population. The risk of disease from dogs is so small that it can *safely* be ignored. Far greater is the risk from road accidents, accidents in the home, aeroplane malfunction or guerrilla warfare.

Dogs defaecate. There can be no denying the unpleasant consequences of a close encounter of the faecal kind. It is however quickly solved by prudent use of a little soap and water. Add to this a little owner care and responsibility to ensure that dogs defaecate either away from people or in a place from which the owners can clear it and the problem diminishes to insignificance.

Dogs wandering loose cause road accidents. This can be a serious problem but a little education reinforced by legislation could, should and would reduce this difficulty.

More positively dogs act as a beneficial force in society. Their obvious value as guide dogs, for police and security work, as shepherds, for entertaining those with a gambling bent is especially important. Dogs also act to support social cripples, those who cannot form adequate human relationships, the lonely and the insecure. Far more important is the dog's role as an adjunct to the normal happy family home. The precise role of the family dog has not been defined.

It is clear however that pet dogs provide a positive force for good in the family. Dogs offer children constant companionship, help them develop responsibility and assist them to deal with the consequences of emotional bonds. The relationship between man and dog could surely not have survived man's social evolution from primitive hunter–gatherer to technocrat if it were not based on a great deal more than a flimsy superficial indulgence. It would seem fatuous to dispense with pet dogs because of the dedicated campaigning of an unrepresentative minority before we have analysed their function or attempted to establish their benefits.

Part Two

Choosing your dog – type or breed

Sometimes a puppy or an adult dog chooses you, in which case you have no decision to make and no problem. A friend, perhaps, has a bitch with a litter and persuades you, or more often your children, to adopt one of the puppies. You may have a friend who for some reason can no longer keep their dog and you are induced to act as a benevolent long-suffering aunt or uncle.

More frequently you make a conscious decision to acquire a dog, in which case you must decide what type of dog to have, a pedigree or a mongrel. You have to consider the advantages and disadvantages of an adult dog against a puppy.

Whilst it is quite impossible to make the decision for you one can indicate some of the things you should contemplate when making your choice. Bringing an adult dog that you do not know into your home, particularly if you have children, is fraught with risk and danger. All too often adults become available either because they have a behavioural or temperamental problem which makes then unsuitable as a household pet or more commonly they have been victims of poor or indifferent owners who have allowed the dog to develop troublesome or dangerous habits which you may find difficult, if not impossible, to rectify. I can of course recall many examples of clients taking strange adult dogs and making a resounding success of the relationship for the benefit of all concerned, but be warned, I can also think of many liaisons that have ended in disaster.

Of course when you have the opportunity to know the dog before accepting it into your home permanently then no problem exists. You either like and get along with it or you refuse to take it.

A word for the dog. I think it is rather sad to see dogs passed from owner to owner, sometimes several owners in rapid succession. The unfortunate creatures become confused, nervous and ill at ease. Better not to try adopting an adult at all unless you feel confident that you can make it work. Adult dogs can often be obtained from animal welfare societies, while adult pedigree dogs are occasionally available from breeders or from breed rescue societies.

For those who prefer a puppy, and I believe this to be the more sensible decision, one must consider the merits of a pedigree or mongrel pup. Pedigree puppies are undoubtedly more expensive but the extra money is proportionately small when compared to the cost of feeding and caring for a dog during its lifetime. They have the added advantage that you know how large they will be, what kind of coat they will carry and to some extent what kind of temperament they will have. Those who favour mongrels believe with some justification that they are healthier – hybrid vigour – and less likely to inherit disease. (See Genetics)

A few observations for the prospective purchaser of a pedigree pup. While you will inevitably be influenced by the type and size of breed you favour, be sure that the dog you choose fits your life style. Whatever the wrapping you will eventually like your dog because of his or her personality. There is little point in getting a St Bernard or a great dane, if you live in a tiny flat, at the top of a tower block, drive a small car and have a demanding job which leaves you little time for dog walking. Conversely for those who sport a large country mansion littered with antiques, drive a Rover, indulge in shooting on Scottish grouse moors, and who require a guard dog for their wife and her diamonds while they are away on international assignments then the choice of a chihuahua or pomeranian could be considered somewhat inept.

For the houseproud or for those with little time or inclination to spend on grooming and washing dogs then a smooth haired breed would seem essential. The desire for a pekinese, old English sheepdog or bearded collie should conversely be coupled with plenty of spare time and a delight in grooming dogs.

The calm phlegmatic human personality appears complemented by a gentle gun dog while the effervescent may prefer one of the terriers.

Whatever type or breed of dog you finally choose be sure the decision is based on practical reality. It should fit your family and your style and the choice should not be influenced by fashion or sentiment.

One dog or two?

We have seen previously that the degree of intimacy achieved with the man/dog relationship is due to the similarities in their social structure – their family or pack units. There are however inevitably certain deficiencies in this relationship due to imperfections of communication between the species. The welfare of domestic dogs is greatly improved by close contact with its own kind. Two dogs are better than one. In my experience no owner who has introduced a second dog to a household which previously had only one, has been in any doubt about the beneficial effects. Old dogs become rejuvenated. Young dogs reared together develop the correct relationships with others of their kind and show complete social integration.

Incidentally one of the problems associated particularly with male dogs – their aberrant sexual approach to children (riding children) – is rarely if ever seen where two dogs, no matter what their sexes, are reared together.

As a bonus for the owners of more than one dog – three or four are even more fun than two – they can enjoy the pleasure of observing the dogs' relationship develop, and watching the dogs play is great fun. Owners can also leave two or three dogs alone together without feelings of guilt.

Q Should both dogs be of the same sex or can one have a male and female?

A For the inexperienced owner it is best to have two bitches. The commonly held belief that two bitches fight is quite fallacious. They may have the odd squabble but it rarely develops into serious combat. The best way of keeping a well adjusted pair together is to allow the bitch to have a litter and then let her keep one of the bitch puppies. The unique bond between mother and offspring is retained into adulthood. The development of this relationship is quite fascinating to observe. (See Male or female?)

If you do have two males ideally they should be of different ages so that the obvious social superiority of the elder is not constantly challenged by the younger. Two dogs can often be kept together successfully but it is more likely to work when placid breeds are kept. Terriers, and classically Staffordshire bull terriers, are likely to pose real and lasting difficulties.

Those who choose or, who for some other reason, are forced to keep a dog and a bitch together obviously face problems associated with their sexual appetites, although the various possibilities of canine contraception discussed elsewhere have largely negated these difficulties. Having kept a male dog together with several bitches one appreciates the extension of the social behaviour between the sexes; one observes with admiration the responsibility assumed by the male for his small pack.

Q If one of the pair dies does the remaining dog show grief and should one replace the loss with a new puppy?

A Grief is a subjective emotion and it is impossible to answer with

Two dogs are better than one

certainty. Certainly many owners in this situation are convinced that the remaining dog demonstrates grief, becoming lethargic and dull. The introduction of a new puppy is quite definitely beneficial to the older dog who 'takes on a new lease of life'.

Male or female?

For those with little experience of dogs or for those with children I have absolutely no hesitation in suggesting – I would like to insist – that they have a bitch. I appreciate there are many male dogs, I know of a great many, who live happily and safely in a family of children and who have never attempted to bite anybody. Conversely I have had to destroy many dogs for savaging children or adults and the majority have been males.

Without delving too deeply into the motivation of aggressive behaviour suffice to say that in the male dog it is intimately related both to their sexuality and their attitude to the social dominance hierarchy. Providing the dog is well handled by competent and experienced owners who are prepared to demand disciplined behaviour then there should be few difficulties with a male dog. Problems arise with novice or nervous owners who are ignorant of, or unprepared to impose, adequate discipline. The relationship between a male dog and its owner is markedly different, being altogether more intense, than that which exists with a bitch.

I would beg inexperienced owners or owners with children to obtain a bitch. (See Solving the problems of female sexuality)

Where should you get a puppy?

Puppies should always come to you direct from the bitch. Ideally you should go to the bitch, select your puppy from her litter and then bring it home with you. You should not buy a puppy from a pet shop. You should not buy a puppy from a dealer. You should insist on seeing the bitch and, if possible, the sire.

Remember, if you will, what you are doing to this tiny scrap. Puppies in nature remain with their mother and with other members of their pack. They gradually develop an awareness of their environment, the limits of their territory. The pack is a close social unit which imposes discipline but which equally offers a deep feeling of security. When you take the puppy it loses its mother, its litter mates and it leaves the only environment it has ever known and in which it feels safe and secure. Is it surprising that the puppy feels a little distressed and insecure?

This act of social aggression, performed so frequently by man, is quite enough for any puppy without adding additional abuse to the poor infant by passing it through dealers' or pet shop owners' hands with the inevitable changes of environment and food, not to mention the increased risk of contacting infection from these premises.

It is a sad reflection on our system of trading that this abuse is allowed to continue uncontrolled by a society which prides itself on being cognizant of the feelings of animals. Many puppies subjected to this dreadful abuse show varying degrees of distress and illness, some die. Puppies brought from the bitch to the home and treated with sympathy and understanding are amazingly able to cope with little apparent ill effect.

Puppy dealing is an evil trade. Some puppies are removed from their mother and taken to a collecting dealer in one part of the country. Within a few days they are moved to a second dealer near to a great metropolis. There they remain until a third dealer, or more fortunately a prospective owner selects them for their final destination. No mammal should be so abused. The incidence of disease and death in puppies so subjected is high, far too high.

There can be no compromise. Go to the bitch yourself. Select the puppy and bring it home with you. Do not let a dealer obtain a puppy for you. Do not have a puppy sent by public transport. Do this important job yourself.

Those who have decided to purchase a pedigree puppy have few problems in Great Britain. A list of reputable breeders can be obtained from the Kennel Club.

Mongrel or cross bred puppies are obtained less formally, but the principle remains. Locate a bitch with puppies through one of the welfare societies or your local veterinary surgeon and go to the owner of the bitch for your puppy.

What age should a puppy leave its mother?

This is a subject about which there are some quite interesting and practically important scientific studies. Konrad Lorenz the famous ethologist honoured with a Nobel prize for his studies in animal behaviour introduced the word 'imprinting' to the scientific world. This phenomenon, which he demonstrated in geese, basically describes the method by which newly hatched goslings learn what their mother looks and sounds like. The first thing they see after hatching, which naturally would be their mother, is followed by the young birds. Imprinting is a very fast reaction in precocious birds. A very similar phenomenon occurs in precocious mammals like sheep and cattle. In dogs, where development of the senses is not so well advanced at birth there is delay in this essential mechanism for social awareness. Known as the period of socialisation it begins at about four weeks of age when the senses are more developed and continues until about fourteen weeks of age. During this period puppies learn to respond socially, learn to recognise their own kind. One of the important factors which allowed dogs to become domesticated so readily is their ability during this important period of socialisation to accept other creatures – notably man – as ones with which to interact socially.

Practically, therefore, a puppy taken from its mother before the onset of this impressionable period and reared only with humans, a situation which occurs when an orphaned puppy is hand reared, has difficulty in recognising itself as a dog. It may show aberrant behaviour as an adult, when confronted by, or forced into close social contact with, another dog. While such animals make adequate pets, difficulties may be experienced if any attempt is made to mate them as they do not recognise dogs as creatures for sexual interaction. Bitches may be very aggressive and dogs may show no enthusiasm for mating.

Conversely puppies left in kennels with little or no close human contact until after the end of the period of socialisation, may find social contact with humans difficult. They may be nervous and hesitant pets. To some extent this can be overcome with careful and sympathetic handling but many continue to show retiring rather inadequate social reaction to strange humans if not to their owners.

A puppy exposed to social contact with both humans and dogs during this formative period develops adequate social relations with both species. From these observations it can be inferred that a puppy removed from its mother too early may make a good pet but may show embarrassingly reticent behaviour towards other dogs while out walking and may be difficult to use for stud. A dog taken into close human contact after this may make a poor pet. Ideally puppies should be taken from their mother at about eight to ten weeks of age having spent some of the period of socialisation in close social contact with dogs but have some of the period left in which to develop adequate relationships with human beings. My personal observations have revealed that dogs which are reared and live in groups are socially well adjusted and show normal sexual behaviour.

How do you choose your puppy?

Choosing a puppy is by no means an easy task. People with years of experience in owning and breeding dogs find it impossible to guarantee either the physical or temperamental future for a puppy. There are however a few guide lines which will help you to choose. For those with little experience it is always useful to solicit the assistance of a friend with more knowledge than you have yourself. It is also very wise to purchase the puppy 'subject to examination by your veterinary surgeon'. Reputable breeders will have no objection to this arrangement. The veterinary examination should be arranged as soon as is practicable. It is unfair to the breeder, and there may be legal difficulties, if you attempt to return a puppy as unsuitable more than a few days after purchase.

From the moment you arrive at the breeder's kennels you should begin your assessment. Do the premises appear clean? Is the owner efficient and businesslike? Are the other dogs you see fond of the breeder? Does the breeder demonstrate empathy with them? Are you given access to the kennels without hesitation or are you asked to wait while the puppies are brought to you? Are you shown the bitch without asking? Are you shown the bitch at all? (Some breeders buy in litters of puppies which immediately converts them into dealers.) (See Where should you get a puppy?)

When you see the puppies they may be in a play period in which case they should be full of uncontrollable bounce or they may have just finished romping, when they will be in a heap together, sound asleep. When sleeping puppies come round, they may take time to wake depending on how long they have been asleep. There should be no 'hangers back'. Healthy puppies are a handful. Like healthy, well-adjusted children they are naughty and full of fun. Do not choose a puppy out of sympathy. The pathetic creature which appears lethargic and nervous, lurking in the corner of the pen, hesitating to approach your offered hand may well have temperamental or health problems. When you have selected one or more puppies on the basis of their temperament in the pen, their colour or their sex, examine them carefully. A healthy puppy is wriggly and friendly. It is plump and soft to the touch without obvious signs of protruding ribs or backbone. The skin should be mobile – you can pick up a handful of skin without distress to the puppy and on release it should flop back into place immediately. The eyes should be bright and clear – beware of the discharge which is explained away by the breeder as due to the sawdust or bedding. Many healthy, well-adjusted puppies will, if given the chance, lick your face or chew your hand. Ears should be clean. The teeth, except in those breeds like bulldogs, boxers, pekinese, etc. which have unusual mouth structure, should meet perfectly. The skin should be clean. Puppies should not keep scratching and should not be sensitive to you scratching their back. The limbs should be strong. Examine the anal region for signs of diarrhoea. Feel the puppy all over for any unusual lump or bump. A swelling in the middle of the abdomen or belly, at the umbilicus or belly button is probably a hernia. This is rarely serious but may need an operation to correct it.

When you are satisfied and have selected your puppy you should endeavour to find out how the puppy has been fed. Most breeders will give you a diet sheet. I have many reservations about some modern methods used to feed puppies these days (See Feeding) but it is advisable to keep to the feeding regime the puppy has been used to for a few days at least. The puppy has enough change to cope with coming to live with you without changing the diet as well.

When you pay for the puppy the breeder should give you a copy of your puppy's pedigree, although many breeders, excellent in all other respects, can be a little lax in this department. This is usually a result of overwork, or omission rather than fraudulent activity, so be gentle but firm and insist that a pedigree be posted to you within a few days. Pedigree puppies should also be accompanied by a transfer certificate from the Kennel Club.

Travelling home
The journey from the kennels to your home must be one of the most

Healthy puppies are a handful

terrifying experiences of your dog's entire life. The puppy has left its mother, its litter mates and its familiar surroundings for the first time. It is travelling in a car, bus or train being held by a strange human – and is hearing the noises of our noxious civilisation for the very first time. Not surprising perhaps that anxiety develops, not surprising that it cries and is eventually sick.

There is not a great deal one can do to alleviate the misery, but a few things may lighten its burden. Wrap the puppy in a warm soft blanket. Have it close to you and comfort it with your voice and by stroking it – tactile sense is very important to young animals and particularly to those with several litter brothers and sisters. If necessary provide warmth – a hot water bottle. Keep the journey as short as possible. Go directly home. Do not drop in on Grandmother to show her your new acquisition. The sooner you get home the sooner the noise and movement will stop, and the sooner the puppy will begin to familiarise itself with its new home.

Q Should the puppy be fed before travelling?

A No. Feed the puppy with a small amount of cereal about an hour after you arrive home. Even puppies on long flights overseas are not fed.

Settling the puppy – the first week

A great deal of nonsense is talked about settling a puppy into your home. You have already been asked to consider the trauma to which your puppy has been subjected by moving it to your house. It has lost the security of its mother and its litter mates. It is an inexperienced baby animal asked to deal with a whole new set of conditions without the support of those it has always been able to rely on. Do not be harsh. Have sympathy and understanding.

Puppies vary considerably in their ability to deal with the move. The confident may even appear to relish the change. Others may show considerable signs of distress. On arrival at your home either sit quietly with the pup for a while or put it in a warm box, wrapped in a blanket or a soft cushion, to sleep. These tactile supports are an attempt to mimic some of the physical attributes of the litter it has so recently lost. When it wakes offer your puppy a drink of warm milk (See Feeding) or a bowl of warm cereal. If it refuses don't worry. If it cries or sits and looks bewildered pick it up and nurse it. If it tries to play – surprisingly some do, then have a gentle game but be careful not to be too rough. It must not be frightened at this stage. The rest of the day should be spent close to the puppy offering company but never forcing too much attention. Children should be well briefed and must be made to harness their natural inclinations to smother the puppy with affection and attention. Puppies, even in the litter, only play for short periods of about half an hour, between long sleeping sessions.

Feeding will depend on the puppy, the journey and the time of day it arrives at your house. If it seems to want its normal food then it can have it by all means. If not, small meals of warm cereal will suffice.

The biggest problem associated with new puppies is the night time. Forced into this terrifying new environment without friends or security the only thing your puppy has is you. It really is extremely severe to expect a puppy to settle down on its own in a new home in a strange bed amidst unusual smells without a 'tear' or two. Take the poor thing to your bedroom for heaven's sake. Put it next to your bed. Give it a hot water bottle. Fondle it if it cries. Understand its feelings. Forget the nonsense you so often hear that once it gets the idea of coming to your bedroom you will never get it to sleep elsewhere. Once it becomes familiar with your house, once it settles and adopts your house and garden as its territory you will easily be able to make it sleep anywhere you like in the house. For the first week or so do all you can to make the puppy accept you as its new pack, do all in your power to give it confidence. There is the old story that a clock ticking by the pup simulates its mother's heart beat, and so subdues fear. It's a nice idea and it certainly can't do any harm, although I suspect it is a little far-fetched – a gentle and harmless touch of witchcraft. A tape recording of the mother's heart beat or the grunts and grumbles of its sleeping litter mates may be more scientific!

The first week has been chosen as a specific period since experience shows that most problems show themselves within seven days. During the first week everything should be done to gain the puppy's trust. Discipline is rarely needed and, when it is, should be of the mildest kind. A harsh word usually suffices.

As soon as possible after purchase the wise owner will ask a veterinary surgeon to examine the puppy to make sure it is sound and healthy. At this time it is useful to discuss any problems that have arisen and to make sure that you are progressing satisfactorily. Veterinary surgeons are, or should be, happy to discuss puppy rearing as they are only too well aware of the importance of a good start. A few corrective words, a little well-timed advice, can prevent greater problems later. I am more than happy for owners to lean heavily on me at this critical time.

It is my practice to ask owners to keep the puppy for about a week before starting the vaccination programme. This ensures that the puppy is over the stress of moving and is well and truly adjusted to its new home.

By the end of the first week in your home the puppy should have settled in. It should be sleeping at nights. Any feeding problems should have been overcome and above all it should show enthusiasm for your company and delight at your attention.

Q What should I do if the veterinary surgeon finds something wrong with the puppy?

A This depends on the severity of the problem and on the cost of correcting it. Discuss your action with the veterinary surgeon. If it is a problem which can be corrected, e.g. persistent hind dew claws or umbilical hernia, you may simply wish to contact the breeder to adjust the price which you have paid. If there is a severe defect, for example congenital heart disease, you will have to decide whether you wish to return the puppy or keep a possible invalid. It is always as well to approach the breeder with courtesy since they will most probably have sold the puppy in good faith and will be as upset as you that one of their puppies is unwell and a genuine customer unhappy. My experience over many years is that on this issue breeders do all in their power to compensate the customer either by offering a replacement puppy or with a refund of purchase money.

Vaccination

It is normal to vaccinate puppies in this country against distemper (and hardpad – two very closely related diseases caused by viruses), canine viral hepatitis and two forms of leptospirosis. (See under separate headings in Part III)

Puppies can be vaccinated from six weeks of age with a second injection given not before it is twelve weeks old and with an interval of at least two weeks between injections. The reason for the two injections and their timing depends on the age at which protection from the mother – maternal antibodies – wears off. In some puppies the mother's protection has disappeared by six weeks. These puppies are therefore at risk and may develop distemper if they are in contact with infection. Other puppies may not lose their mother's protection until the twelfth week. Only then are they at risk. Maternal antibodies prevent active immunisation of a puppy. We are therefore in the difficult position of having some puppies at risk from six weeks and others not at risk until they are twelve weeks. Unfortunately we do not know which individuals are which in the consulting room. To make sure that all puppies have as much protection as possible at this high risk period of their lives, the vaccination programme in general use has been devised. Puppies are given a first injection at between six and eight weeks. In those puppies which still retain maternal antibodies the distemper part will clearly be of no value. However in those puppies which have lost their mother's protection this injection will do what all vaccinations do, give the protective mechanism of the body a very mild taste of the disease and allow it to build up the weapons – the specific antibodies – which are needed to deal with this kind of germ. It is clearly important to protect those puppies which retain their mother's antibodies until they are twelve weeks of age. A second injection is therefore given at twelve weeks, when research work tells us we can be sure that all puppies are completely clear of the maternal protective antibodies.

Sometimes, because of late purchase or because owners have been given rather archaic information by breeders, puppies are not brought to the surgery for vaccination until twelve weeks of age, when the maternal antibodies will have definitely disappeared from the puppy. In this case the distemper vaccine will take and should be followed by a second injection of leptospirosis and canine viral hepatitis, both of which always have to be given twice, two weeks later.

If the protective mechanisms of the body are not constantly reminded of the kind of germ they have to deal with they become inefficient. It is customary to remind them with frequent re-vaccination, the booster.

Every dog should be re-vaccinated yearly. Some veterinary surgeons alternate re-vaccinations. One year, vaccine against all diseases are given. The alternate year injection against leptospirosis and canine viral hepatitis are given. This is strictly quite correct because the distemper vaccine lasts well over one year. Other veterinary surgeons, and this is my practice, prefer to re-vaccinate against all infections every year.

Q When vaccination first came out years ago, it was said to last a lifetime. Why has there been a change?

A Years ago when vaccination was introduced, initially against distemper only, there was a great deal of the virus about in the environment. The few puppies which were vaccinated to protect them against the disease would almost certainly have had their artificial protection challenged by natural virus with which they would have come in contact. Although the original vaccination would not have lasted a lifetime, in practice it would have protected them against the first contacts with the virus. The natural virus would then have acted as a booster vaccine by constantly keeping the body's protective mechanism vigilant. To-day as a result of vaccination there is very little distemper virus in the environment and most dogs have no contact with natural infection. Without re-vaccination the body's protective mechanism would become idle. It would forget how to make the specific antibodies it needs to protect itself against distemper. Sudden challenge by a local outbreak of distemper would find it unprepared, and the dog, even old dogs, would succumb.

The same reasons apply for the re-vaccination of the other diseases.

Q There are two types of canine viral hepatitis vaccine, live attenuated and killed. What is the difference and which should be used when?

A There has been much discussion on this issue in the canine press. In general a live attenuated virus vaccine is more effective in producing immunity than the killed virus. Distemper for an example is now produced as a freeze-dried vaccine of living attenuated virus. The difficulty with canine viral hepatitis is that to date the living attenuated virus when used as a vaccine can produce some unpleasant side effects – more common, it seems, in some breeds than others. While the risk from this type of vaccine is small a number of veterinary surgeons prefer to use the safer, but it has to be admitted less effective, killed vaccine. It is to be hoped that further research will eliminate the small number of problems currently experienced by the use of living attenuated canine viral hepatitis vaccine.

Q When can the puppy go out after vaccination?

A Two weeks after effective protection against distemper. In practice this means two weeks after the injection given at twelve weeks. Whether it be the first or second vaccination we can be sure that in all puppies the twelfth-week injection will take. When for some reason the normal programme is not followed and vaccination is started after twelve weeks, then two weeks should elapse from the time of the first distemper vaccination until contact with other dogs is allowed.

Q Can the dog go in the garden?

A Yes. Although there is always a slight risk even in your own garden, in practice it is very small. If you do not let it into the garden you may have problems with house training and you could well produce a very nervous puppy. For the same reason it would be as well to take the puppy for car rides to accustom it to the strange vehicle and to the outside world. This again is quite safe so long as you do not allow the puppy out to run the risk of infection. I would also recommend carrying the puppy for short distances – great danes, wolfhounds and St Bernards of necessity sadly excluded – away from your home to acquaint him with the various aspects of the outside world.

Q Should you take a puppy not fully protected to a house with another dog, and how much risk is there if you already have a dog yourself?

A The risk of contact with one or two dogs which are themselves fully vaccinated is small. I always advise people not to worry if a visit to Granny and her dog is planned. If you already have a dog yourself, the puppy will rarely, if ever, come to any harm. Indeed from a behavioural standpoint contact with other dogs during the period up to fourteen weeks of age is essential if they are to become well orientated, adjusted, dogs able to enjoy adequate social relationships with others of their kind. (See What age should the puppy leave its mother?) It is essential to balance risk of infection against behavioural development.

Q Why do we not vaccinate puppies against rabies in the U.K.?

A We are fortunate in this country to be free of this dreadful disease and we are fortunate in being an island. Hopefully the quarantine laws and the vigilance of the Ministry of Agriculture will maintain this situation. Vaccination is only used when a disease is already widespread in a country. The danger of vaccination is firstly that no vaccination is one hundred per cent effective, and secondly that it can produce so-called carrier states in some animals which would then act to infect others although they themselves would not show symptoms.

Q Why do we not vaccinate puppies against tetanus?

A Dogs are very resistant to tetanus. Unlike horses and sheep they are very rarely infected with the disease. It would be quite pointless and totally uneconomic to vaccinate dogs against this disease.

Routine worming

Irresponsible journalism has created an unseemly hysteria about the danger to children from roundworms. (See Part 1, Dogs in modern society)

Puppies and adult dogs should however be wormed both to ensure that they do not suffer the ill effects of these parasites and to virtually eliminate the very, very small risk that would otherwise exist for children with whom the dogs have contact.

Opinions differ considerably about worming programmes. Ideally a bitch should be wormed before she is mated. This will help to eliminate or reduce the worm burden of her puppies. The bitch should not be wormed during gestation, i.e. while she is carrying her pups. The puppies should be wormed as directed by a veterinary surgeon. Some suggest that all dogs should then be wormed at monthly intervals for the rest of their lives. In practice however I feel satisfied if my clients dose their dogs every six months.

Worm doses can be obtained from a veterinary surgeon or as a proprietary drug from pharmacists. In general the former method is to be preferred since it enables the veterinary surgeon to modify a regime to the needs of local conditions and to the condition of your dog. The veterinary surgeon can also test your dog to establish the state of its worm burden, and if necessary can alter the frequency of dosage.

Q Should a dog be dosed routinely for tapeworm?

A Tapeworms are less common than roundworms. They cause very few problems to the dog and are no risk to children. Tapeworm need only be treated if its presence is diagnosed. If you have any doubt about the type of worm your dog has take a sample to your veterinary surgeon who will be able to tell at a glance.

Feeding

More nonsense is talked about feeding dogs by the self-appointed dog 'experts', who litter every bar room and coffee morning, than almost any other subject. It is with great regret that these 'experts' who always seem to make such an impression on one's client, dispense more munch mythology than reasoned observation. The interjection of the pet food industry with its panache for misleading advertisements has further complicated what is essentially a very straightforward story.

Dogs are carnivores. They eat other animals. Wolves and wild dogs are first reared on their mothers' milk and are weaned onto food regurgitated from the stomachs of their mothers and other members of the pack. For the rest of their lives they eat the flesh of large herbivores, supplemented in times of hardship with small rodents and even some fruit and vegetable matter.

When wolves and dogs kill they consume the whole carcass including partially digested vegetable matter in the gut of their victim. There is no evidence that domestication has altered the needs of the dog and its ability to digest this basic canine diet. I recommend pet mince from your butcher.

Feeding puppies

Puppies of wild dogs begin to beg for regurgitated food from their mother and other pack members from four or five weeks of age. They do this by licking the faces of adults until they are rewarded with a well chewed pile of vomit which they then consume with relish. There are obvious advantages. The pups could not go hunting with adult members of the pack, being far too small. The adult could not drag a huge carcass back to the den to provide pups with food. They therefore wisely store some food for the pups in their stomach where it remains secure and warm. In addition it is partially digested by the adults' gastric juices before the pups eat it.

Pet puppies will beg for food from their mothers and will often be rewarded with a warm regurgitated meal. Because most people find this natural method rather anti-social and perhaps more important because in most cases the bitch will be separated from its puppies, as they are sold to new homes soon after weaning, a simple, convenient and well tried method of feeding young puppies has been devised. One or two simple facts upon which to muse. Puppies have a rapid growth rate. They need, relative to the size of their body, more food than an adult, because in addition to maintaining their daily needs they have to eat enough to fuel their growth. Their stomach, again relative to body size, is no longer than that of an adult. They must therefore eat more frequently. Hence while an adult can be maintained on one meal each day, puppies must eat several meals in the same period.

Feeding puppies is quite simple. From weaning until it is about four months of age a puppy should have four meals a day. Two of the meals should be a mixture of meat, and I mean meat – fresh mince is ideal – not synthetic substitutes from tins, packets or plastic bags, together with wholemeal bread or one of the better puppy biscuit meals commercially available. The other two meals should consist of a milk-based cereal food. Some of the well-balanced cereals produced for human babies are excellent for puppies. It has become fashionable among the dog fraternity fo decry the use of cows' milk for puppies. Apart from the very few puppies which are allergic to cows' milk and which therefore require milk substitutes this concern is totally unfounded. I have been rearing puppies on cows' milk for some thirty years without ill effect.

It is best to alternate these two types of meal. Early morning

(7–9 a.m.) give a milk-based cereal. Mid-morning (12–2 p.m.), meat and toasted wholemeal bread or biscuits. Late afternoon (5–7 p.m.) the second milk-based cereal. Evening, (9–11 p.m.) the second meat and wholemeal bread or puppy biscuit. The late meal before bed helps to settle the puppy for the night. It is of value to substitute scrambled egg for the first milk feed of the morning two or three times a week.

Appropriate doses of vitamins A and D should be given to young pups. Between three to four months of age one of the milk-based cereal meals should be discontinued. Often the puppy itself indicates a lack of interest in one of the meals, usually breakfast. Quantities of food should be increased gradually to accommodate the growing dog.

From six months to nine months of age two meals are sufficient, both consisting of meat with toasted wholemeal bread or dog biscuit.

After nine months the second meal should be discontinued. One meal of meat, wholemeal bread or dog biscuits is then sufficient.

Q How much should I feed my dog?

A It is quite impossible to give exact figures. Just like people, some dogs can eat enormous amounts of food without getting fat, while others seem to bulge in the wrong places on very moderate consumption. As a rough guide a puppy of the smaller breeds will need no more than an ounce or two of meat daily while adults of the larger breeds may consume up to two pounds of meat. Excessive quantities of pure meat may cause diarrhoea so if the dog appears thin increase the cereal part of its diet – wholemeal bread or dog biscuit. If it is overweight reduce the cereal.

One of the commoner mistakes found in dog feeding is the 'once and for all' attitude where a set amount of food is given every day regardless of need. The food requirement of a dog varies throughout its life. It needs more food when young than when adult. More in winter than summer. Bitches' needs vary with their sexual cycle and so on. The good dog owner keeps constant vigil and varies the amount of food with the condition of the dog. All dogs should have a recognisable waist but the ribs should be covered. (See Obesity)

Q Should puppies be given seaweed tablets, garlic, added calcium, bone meal, condition tablets, yeast, ground spiders' legs, etc.

A No. Puppies provided with a decent varied diet of good quality food, do not benefit from these fashionable feeding foibles promoted by so many of the dog 'experts'. They are at best a waste of money and at worst detrimental to the animal's welfare, in some cases themselves causing disease.

Q Do adults need seaweed tablets, garlic, added calcium, bone meal, condition tablets, yeast, ground spiders' legs, frogs' toes, etc., etc?

A No.

Q Tinned dog food and synthetic dried whole foods are recommended by many breeders. Can they be used in place of meat and wholemeal bread?

A Prepared dogs foods, the so-called pet foods, can and are used by many owners exclusively. I believe that dogs are better fed on fresh meat and that tinned and other synthetic foods be restricted to useful stand-bys for weekend or holiday periods. I believe my own dogs keep in better condition on fresh meat.

Q Is fish good for dogs?

A Certainly fish can be used to vary the diet of dogs. It can be used occasionally to replace the meat content of the diet both in puppies and adults. Variety is the spice of life.

Q Should a dog have bones?

A There is no doubt that dogs enjoy bones. They are, however, certainly not essential for health and there is no evidence that they have any effect in keeping teeth clean. If bones are given at all they should be raw marrow bones. Cooked bones of any kind are dangerous because they become brittle and splinter. Particularly dangerous are poultry, rabbit and chop bones. Some large powerful dogs can grind even marrow bones into a powder, which sets like cement in the intestine and causes obstruction. In general I prefer the commercially available hide chews to bones. If you do give bones remember dogs become very possessive about them. Be careful the dog does not attack children who venture near when a dog has a bone. Train your dog from a puppy to let you remove the bone from it.

Obesity

Dogs are dogs not Dumbos. Western man shares with his dog the effects of affluence. Both have a strong tendency to obesity.

Obesity has a number of deleterious effects on health, causes constant physical and mental distress to the afflicted and is unaesthetic for the observer. Fat dogs are inclined to live shorter lives, suffer from heart and blood vessel conditions, skin disease, kidney and liver dysfunction, and arthritis. Surgery, if required, carries an increased risk, wound healing may be impaired and recovery prolonged. Fat dogs are less inclined to take exercise because of the distressing effects of panting, overheating and breathlessness coupled, in some extreme cases, with physical impairment of limb movement.

Dogs become fat for one reason and for one reason only, they *eat too much*. No amount of selfdeception by owners, no amount of incoherent mumbling about hormones, spaying, lack of exercise or old age disguises the reality that fat dogs are fat because they eat too much. Whenever one suggests to a client that their dog is overweight one stimulates a stereotyped conversation which has been repeated verbatim hundreds of times. The accused owners first offer every kind of excuse, then indulge in the most blatant deceptions and finally pursue the most unlikely avenue of evasion rather than face the reality that their dog is fat because it eats too much.

Nearly all dogs will overeat given the chance. Nature has designed it that way. In the wild dogs eat when they kill, spasmodically. They may go several days between meals so they are able to consume more at a sitting than they require for immediate needs. They store the extra as fat for leaner times. It is a well-designed system for the wild. Domestication has not altered the system. Pet dogs eat more than they need and store the rest as fat for leaner times. The problem is there never are leaner times. Every day is bountiful. Every day excess food is stored as fat. Owners must therefore restrict their dogs' daily intake. Each dog must be given each day only that amount required for immediate use. Owners do the storing in the tin or in the fridge. The problem is of course exacerbated because one of the pleasures of keeping dogs is the reward obtained from feeding and nurturing the dog. It is nice to feel needed. It is all too easy to gratify one's own needs to the detriment of the dog.

Feeding the dog is an art based on science, not a pure science. Most owners will explain graphically how much food they give their dog. Herein lies one problem. Quantities should not be rigidly fixed but must vary according to the line and look of the dog. If it is too thin the food is increased. If it is too fat then the amount is decreased. It is as simple and straightforward as that!

Once a dog has become overweight it becomes difficult to persuade, it often becomes impossible to persuade, an owner to put the dog on a diet. Many, many owners appear to comprehend one's logic, share one's concern for the health of their dog, apparently listen and indicate that they understand the mechanics of dieting, offer profuse thanks for one's interest, assure one that they will follow the advice to the letter and then go away to do exactly as they have always done, overfeed their dog. Months later they have the audacity to return to the consulting room with the dog unchanged or several sizes larger, and looking one straight in the eye say that one's advice has not worked. If the dog's food intake is reduced to below that needed for maintenance the dog will have to mobilise its store of fat; it will have to lose weight. Fat men didn't stay fat in Belsen long!

For those with a real determination to diet their dog, seek veterinary advice. Weigh the dog or measure its girth and record it. Cut down the food. Cut out the tit bits. Weigh or measure carefully the food you give. If the dog doesn't lose weight you are still giving too much. Reduce the food again. Indeed continue to reduce the quantities until you do see positive results. Remember dieting is a slow, often laborious, task. Don't lose heart after a week. Your reward for success will be a slim, aesthetically pleasing, healthy dog, a joy to own and a joyful companion.

Bedding

The dog is an undemanding creature. It asks little for its comfort. It is however in its interests for you to provide a comfortable draughtproof bed.

A wide variety of commercially produced dog beds are readily available. Many of these are excellent in design and are more pleasing to the eye than a cardboard or wooden box. They are often raised from the ground which helps to keep dogs out of draughts and reduces dampness by keeping the bed ventilated.

Many of the synthetic materials used for dog beds are extremely warm and comfortable and have the added advantage that they can be machine washed. Beware of foam rubber for dog beds, particularly when used for puppies. They have a tendency to chew it, occasionally with fatal results.

In spite of a natural affinity with traditional materials and ancient skills, I do not believe basketwork is a good material for dog beds. It is not draughtproof, is not hygenic and may cause considerable trouble if chewed.

Clothing

Clothing for dogs is an abomination. Those who wish to dress up their dogs to gratify some personal frustration would be better off with one of the excellent toy dolls currently available which come complete with clothing sets. Dogs do not need to wear coats, unless, for very limited periods, medical opinion dictates.

Kennelling

There is no reason why the larger, heavy-coated breeds cannot live in an outdoor kennel, providing it is waterproof and draughtproof, and has a thick bed of straw or several layers of dry blanket. Smaller breeds and those with smooth fine coats, large or small, are not able to conserve their body heat adequately enough for cold winters, and should not be expected to live outside.

In addition to the kennel itself, which should be just large enough to allow the dog to lie comfortably, adequate provision for movement and exercise must be available. Free range of the garden is ideal but a large wired-in run will suffice providing the dog gets regular exercise in the form of walks. If a wire run is provided then it should be well built with care to make sure the dog does not injure itself and the floor should be of concrete with a slight slope for easy cleaning.

The kennel can be made of brick or one of the modern substitute blocks. These should be rendered on the inside with concrete. Brick built kennels have the advantage of being hygienic and easily cleaned but suffer from the disadvantage of being somewhat cold and damp. For warmth and comfort wood is ideal but is not so easily disinfected, although many of the modern commercially available wood kennels are excellent.

While there is nothing wrong with keeping suitable dogs outside, kennelling is usually restricted to the working dog or for commercial breeding or boarding kennels. A good relationship with a pet dog is enhanced by close contact and this is more likely to be achieved by keeping the dog in the house. I would not advise a pet dog owner to contemplate an outside kennel unless there are pressing personal circumstances which make it inevitable.

Q. What size should the run be?

A. The run should be as large as possible but the length should not be less than six times, and the width twice, the length of the dog.

House training

House training can be a simple task easily achieved or it can be a lengthy business accompanied by frustration and anger. Encouragingly, most dogs, not all but most, are eventually house trained.

A few basic facts may help to understand the puppies' difficulties. Primarily it must be remembered that very small puppies have no more control over their bodily functions than a human baby. As soon as defaecation or urination is stimulated within the body so the process is activated. Conscious control over these functions is only slowly achieved. It is pointless to chastise a puppy under three months of age.

Puppies should not be trained first to newspaper and then to the garden, it is far too confusing. Having learnt what it believes is expected of it – to use the paper – the owner appears to have a brain storm and suddenly and quite irrationally, as far as the puppy is concerned, expects it to use another place, the garden. In addition paper-trained animals may have occasional lapses even as adults and are quite likely to pass an excretary comment upon any newspaper left lying untidily around the house.

House training should begin as soon as you acquire your puppy. From the start be patient, be very patient. Concentrate on congratulating the puppy when it does well and modify your frustration when you begin to think you will never succeed. Put the puppy out in the garden and wait with it. At first it will feel strange, and will not have in mind what you have in mind. As it learns its way around the garden it will develop a sense of security, even territory, and will become relaxed enough to perform the appointed task. Early difficulties are usually due to feelings of insecurity, thus it is important to get the puppy used to the garden as soon as possible. Do not leave it outside alone. It will feel abandoned and frightened and will spend its time crying at the door instead of exploring the rose beds.

As soon as the task is complete be very free with your admiration of its brilliance; positively shower it with praise, both verbal – the tone of voice is important, so be genuine – and tactile, pat it. Dogs like to please and when they grasp quite what it is you want they will do all they can to earn your praise. If you are having difficulties with home training, think about the dog's problems. Imagine yourself as a dog. It will usually help you to understand why things are going wrong.

The other side of training is punishment. When the puppy performs in the house then a gruff, severe voice is usually all that is needed to indicate your displeasure. If you are sure that the puppy understands what it should be doing and is being disobedient then grasp the scruff of the neck and give a very gentle shake. (See Training and discipline)

When house training put the puppy out frequently to forestall any mishap. It is traditional to put puppies out as soon as they wake and immediately they have been fed and the owner is well advised to do this. Recent behavioural research has shown however that puppies frequently defaecate in the middle of their play periods (puppies play frantically for half an hour and then sleep for an hour) and it may well improve training if they are also put out ten minutes after play starts. Puppies often begin to circle, back end first, when about to defaecate. Careful anticipation may save you problems.

Do not expect your puppy to be trained quickly or suddenly. It can be a lengthy process usually taking several weeks. It can extend into months. Even a good pupil will have occasional relapses just like human babies. Verbal disapproval tempered with patience, not physical violence, is essential at such times.

Q Can rolled-up newspaper be used in place of shaking?

A Beating with a rolled-up newspaper either engenders play or aggression. It is not a good agent of discipline.

Q Should you rub a puppy's nose in its mess?

A No. This is an unkind and unnecessary method favoured by ignorant old wives. I have seen the eyes of flat-faced breeds (pekinese, pugs, etc.) damaged by this method. Don't do it!

Exercise

Exercise has two functions. It keeps the dog in good physical condition. Equally important, it provides mental stimulation and prevents boredom.

To ensure good physical condition a dog should have adequate, and above all, regular exercise. A long walk once a month is no substitute for shorter but regular daily walks. Ideally dogs should go to open, preferably country, areas and be allowed free to run and to explore. Free running dogs cover three or four times the distance you cover. Where safety necessitates that a dog remains on a lead then a good brisk walk is better than a slow plod. A word of common sense so often ignored by owners. Although regular walks are ideal there is no need to be a slave to the walk. If you or your dog is ill forget it. If the weather is bad and you are elderly, stay by the fire. It is surprising how often people are prepared to make themselves ill rather than the dog miss a walk, and it is amazing how often people insist on a sick or injured dog taking its constitutional. Just like us when dogs are feeling a little off colour, a little fragile, the last thing they want to do is go out.

As well as the real physical benefits of exercise, a walk provides the

There can be no doubt about the enjoyment of a free-running dog

dog with considerable mental stimulation. Anyone who has watched the enthusiasm and evident joy with which a dog anticipates a walk can be left in no doubt about its beneficial affect. Smell is considerably more important to dogs than to us and we are quite unable to appreciate the pleasure they gain from liberal use of their nose, but even casual observation of their exploratory activities will leave one enjoying their obvious delight.

Where possible walks should be varied. Daily walks around a municipal recreation ground must eventually pall. Dogs like to explore new ground so whenever possible get them away from concrete and the sterility of suburban grass to the excitement of some real country.

Training and discipline

A well trained and disciplined dog is a delight to own. A badly behaved dog is at best a nuisance and at worst a positive danger.

Remember dogs are wolves in fancy dress. They have all the behavioural tendencies of wolves and are therefore ready to accept, indeed feel happier when subjected to, pack discipline. Since pet dogs consider you and your family to be its pack, they respond accordingly.

Training starts as soon as you get your puppy. The first essential is to establish a close relationship with it. The puppy must learn to respect you and to enjoy your company. This essential sympathy is achieved rapidly if you spend time with it, care for it, play games with it and nurse it. Once your puppy accepts you as a substitute dog, a

pack member, it will want to please you. You have now established a good foundation for training.

Dogs are trained by reward and punishment – so called operant conditioning. The first essential for all animal training is understanding and patience. Never lose your temper. Always try to think like a dog. If the dog seems to be slow to understand make certain you have given a clear instruction. Make sure the dog understands what you want it to do.

In most cases dogs can be trained simply with reward. Punishment needs to be only of the mildest form. Turning away from the puppy, ignoring it, is enough to concentrate its mind on the job in hand. Occasionally a sharp, severe word is needed. Corporal punishment is reserved for real disobedience or for any show of aggression, and when administered, care must be taken never to injure the puppy. Remember its size relative to yours. The best way of chastising a puppy is to grasp it gently by the scruff of the neck and give it a little shake. This closely resembles the bitch's method which is to clasp the puppy around the neck with her mouth.

Without doubt the most important lesson which should be learnt very early in life is for the puppy to come when called. Choose the dog's name as soon as you get it and then stick to it. You will only confuse it by changing its name after a few weeks. A short one-syllable name is best. From the start call the pup's name using a gentle tone of voice. At the same time perform a physical movement to attract the pup's attention which suggests to it that a game is imminent. Hold your arms open, slap your leg or waggle your fingers on the ground. If the pup comes make a great fuss of it, telling it how clever it is. If it fails to come increase the intensity of your gyrations. Never lose your temper. If the pup still fails to come, turn and walk away. This is a punishment for a puppy who is fond of its owner, and will usually produce the desired response even in the puppy who is just being purposefully difficult. Repeat the lesson frequently but as with any training session never go on for long or the puppy will become disinterested. You must never let the puppy become bored.

One difficulty in training puppies is the limitations placed on outings by the vaccination programme. Until it is complete the puppy must not mix with strange dogs or be allowed to run in places where dogs have been. During a critical period of the puppy's development, therefore, when it should be learning about its environment, the

Mrs Richards demonstrates obedience training with her border collie.

demands of the vaccination programme actively restrict its experience. To overcome this, carry your puppy for short periods around the streets and through the woods. The puppy will in this way experience a wider environment, lose its fear of new things and will be a bolder puppy without risking infection.

As soon as vaccination is over you can start to take the puppy out for a walk. Before you do, get it used to a lead and collar. A light collar and lead are best for training. Put the collar on for short periods several times each day. Once it has become accustomed to this, attach the lead. Many puppies will take readily to the lead. Those that do not can be induced to walk by holding the end of the lead and calling the puppy to you. It will soon get used to it. For the very difficult pup associate the lead with good things, like a ride in the car or a tit bit.

Early training includes teaching the puppy its place in your home. It must learn where it can and cannot go. I have never seen the point of having a dog and then restricting it to the kitchen. However if you do want to keep the dog downstairs or off the furniture then give clear indications to your puppy but do not expect it to stay on its own for hours in the kitchen while you goggle at the box, drink gin in the lounge or spring clean the bedrooms. A puppy needs company and it needs to play.

Once the puppy has become thoroughly accustomed to walking on the lead it should be taught to walk quietly to heel. Dogs which pull are exhausting and embarrassing to exercise. As the dog pulls forward, tug the lead and ejaculate sharply 'heel'. The dog will of course be pulled thus into place by your side but will soon pull forward again. As soon as he moves ahead of you repeat the command and the tug on the lead thereby putting him back in his correct position. The lesson may take time. It certainly will not be learnt perfectly in one afternoon. Patience is the key word. Dogs who fail to learn can be placed on a large linked choke chain, designed for training.

A dog can be made to sit on demand quite easily. With the dog standing by your side place a hand on its hind quarters and say 'sit' at the same time pressing down with your hand forcing the dog into the sitting position. Following on from this you can make the dog lie down on command by pulling his forelegs from under him at the same time saying 'down'. In all cases repeat the lesson with frequency, and above all with patience.

In addition you should get the puppy used to grooming from an early age and make sure that it allows you to examine all parts of its body at will. If as a puppy it shows some reluctance for example to having its feet examined or its mouth opened, then insist on examining its feet or opening its mouth once or twice every day until all resistance is overcome. It is equally important that dogs allow you to take anything out of their mouth be it ball, bone or baby. Insist on this from the very beginning. Removal of unsuitable material from a dog's mouth may save an emergency operation or even its life.

So long as a dog allows its owner to examine it thoroughly and to groom it, and providing it comes when called, walks obediently to heel when instructed, sits on command and behaves well in the home, I believe both parties can be satisfied with the degree of discipline. There are those who would take obedience training further. For such owners, participation in the many obedience trials through dog training clubs can be an absorbing and demanding hobby. It is as well to choose one of the breeds best suited temperamentally to the task, like border collies or alsatians. Headstrong terriers, boisterous boxers, or independent-minded bull breeds will not share your enthusiasm for obedience trials.

Q Is it wise to send dogs away to schools for training?

A No. Discipline is based on a dynamic relationship between two individuals, a human and a dog. The response of the dog depends on the personality of the owner. Dogs are best trained by encouraging and directing its desire to please its owner. Impersonal training relies on subduing the spirit of the dog, it is destructive rather than constructive and will not achieve the best results and the methods used are questionable. Train your dog yourself.

    A puppy destined to become a police dog is reared by the police constable who is to be its handler throughout its active service life. Secondhand training is not used.

It is true some specialised kind of training – gun dogs, guide dogs for the blind – is undertaken by specialists. Breeds used for this work are carefully selected for their particular behavioural qualities but even so specialised training is not commenced until the puppy has matured in a home environment.

Q Is it advisable to go with a dog to weekly training classes?

A This is a good idea for those who lack confidence. Training classes are essentially for the owner not the dog. They teach the owner how to train a dog. They are also useful in assisting dogs who are antisocial, either timid or aggressive, with other dogs.

Grooming

Grooming is an important part of the routine of dog owning, being particularly important in long-haired breeds. The dog's ancestors, wolves, have thick dense coats, but they do not have long coats which can become tangled or matted. The wolf's coat is kept in good condition by the wolf itself, using its small incisor teeth, and also as a result of social grooming between members of the pack. In addition the natural moulting pattern of two rapid moults each year keeps the coat in good condition.

The purpose of grooming is twofold. Combing and brushing combine to remove tangled or matted hair and to keep the coat clean and free from dirt and improve the dog's social acceptance. In addition brushing is said to stimulate the skin, although this would be very hard to prove scientifically. Wolves and wild dogs manage quite well without such administrations. Daily grooming has therefore become essential as a direct result of the domestication and the development of breeds with long hair unknown in wild dogs and wolves.

Instruments for grooming are simple. A good metal comb with emphasis on the good – it should not have sharp-ended teeth which can cut or otherwise damage the skin – and a stiff bristle brush. The latter will obviously vary in size and stiffness depending on the type of fur to be groomed.

The process of grooming is quite straightforward. Long-haired coats should first be combed to remove tangles. Very fine-coated dogs like pointers, dobermanns, danes, smooth-haired dachshunds, will not need combing at all. They should only be brushed in the direction in which the hair lies.

A shine can be produced on the coat by giving it a final rub with a piece of silk or soft cloth.

Preparation for shows

The preparation of dogs for shows is a subject shrouded in myth and mystery. It varies with each breed. Much of it is nonsense but if you have a bent for the show ring and are inclined to subject your dog to its tortures, you would do well to gain the confidence of an experienced exhibitor from whom you may glean the secrets.

Poodles

Poodles have been selectively bred for their fur. In order to keep them in good condition they should be bathed and trimmed every four to six weeks. Many owners maintain their poodle in reasonable condition on a do-it-yourself basis but for the best results a trained poodle stripper should be employed.

Stripping and trimming

Some breeds like the cocker spaniel need a light trim to keep certain parts of the coat in order, while others notably the wire-haired terriers and related terriers require extensive stripping.

Some owners have the kindly but misguided habit of clipping and shearing the coats of breeds which should never be cut. The cocker spaniel is a good example. This breed should have the feathering on its legs and the hair between its toes cut only. It must not be shorn. Terrier coats should be hand stripped for best results. The use of clippers is cheaper and for the lazy. It is not correct.

Some breeds like the old English sheepdog require a great deal of grooming. Less than diligent owners allow their dog's hair to become matted. This in turn causes smells and discomfort for the dog. The task of reclamation includes, in this case, shearing. Shearing the hair of an old English sheepdog in the summer may be justified.

Correct advice about trimming can be obtained from most veterinary practices or from a competent dog stripper. Remember anybody can be a dog stripper. There is no professional qualification.

Nail clipping

Owners often approach veterinary surgeons to clip the nails of their dog. In fact very few dogs need their nails cut, as so frequently pointed out nobody runs around with nail clippers rendering manicures to wolves and wild dogs. The fact that dogs' nails hurt and scratch when they jump up is no reason to cut the nails. Better discipline is the solution. Don't let them jump up. Cutting the nails will not solve the problem.

Some nails appear longer than others. It depends on the conformation of the nail in relation to the toe. The nail wears to a point level with the ground. If the nail is close to the toe it seems short. If it is away from the toe it looks long.

A 'quick' runs down part of the nail. This has a blood and nerve supply. A quarter of an inch of nail should extend below the quick. If a nail is cut too close to the quick it will be painful, any shorter and it will bleed.

A few old dogs need their nails cut as do some with structure deformity of the feet. Before cutting nails ask your veterinary surgeon's advice. Dogs hate having their nails cut. It may be the noise they object to or the pinching of the quick.

Bathing

Old wives and their endless tales of gloom and misconception are verbose on the subject of bathing dogs. The simple answer to how often and when to bath the dog is whenever it needs it. It is true that oil in the coat protects the dog against the elements. It is therefore with some justification that dogs expected to live in the open would be detrimentally affected by frequent bathing with oil removing soaps and detergents. Most pet dogs are not so subjected. They live in warm, often centrally heated, houses well protected from the ravishes of the elements. I therefore repeat dogs may be bathed just as often as one wishes, indeed some skin conditions, in some breeds of dog, result simply from a dirty ill-kept coat. Conversely there is no need to bath dogs which maintain a clean coat. Many dogs which are kept well groomed go for years without the need for a bath.

Small dogs are easily accommodated for this unwelcome abuse, for few dogs enjoy the procedure, in a small bowl or sink. Large breeds can be placed in the bath or if there is some local reluctance to share the family plunge pot with tte dog then quite satisfactory results can be obtained by standing the dog outside on concrete and pouring warm water over it, followed by a good shampoo and completed with a good rinse. Always be sure that the shampoo is well rinsed out as the residue can irritate the skin.

As soon as dogs are released from their watery torture, they will want to shake. While this is perfectly all right outside it can cause devastation in the house. Rapid swathing in towels will prevent its worst effects. Dogs can be dried with towels, hair driers or by being left in a warm room. Beware of the natural inclination of dogs to cover themselves in a camouflage of antisocial odour. Many dogs if let loose after a bath will roll on the ground, or something even worse if it is available. This can be prevented by keeping them in the house or on a short lead until drying is complete.

Q Should dog shampoos be used for dogs?

A There is no necessity to use special dog shampoos. Any mild human shampoo is satisfactory. Dog shampoos are however very useful.

Q Is it wise to use medicated shampoos?

A Medicated shampoos should only be used on the advice of a veterinary surgeon.

Canine sexuality – female

Female dogs or bitches usually come 'on heat' or into 'oestrus' twice a year. There is however considerable variation both in breeds and individuals. There is no need for alarm if your bitch only comes on heat once every nine months or even every year. It is just normal biological variation and the bitch will come to no harm.

Most bitches begin to come on heat when between six to nine months of age but again there is no need for concern if this is delayed until they are a year or even eighteen months old.

One finds most bitches come on heat in late winter or very early spring and again in the summer. Puppies are born therefore either in the spring or late summer, early autumn.

The heat period manifests itself by a swelling of the vulva and the loss of blood. Bleeding is due to the shedding of the lining of the womb or uterus in preparation for implantation of the placenta and continues for at least ten days. During this period the bitch will not allow a dog to mate with her. She will however be attractive to male dogs and she will pass frequent drops of urine if allowed to go for walks. This urine is apparently very descriptive of her impending condition and is designed to enthuse the local suitors. From about the tenth to the fourteenth day the bitch is at peak of acceptance. It is at this time she is most prepared to stand to be served by a dog, and it is now that the eggs are shed by the ovary and the behavioural inclination of the bitch therefore ensures maximum fertility. From the fourteenth day the bitch's interest in males wanes and the heat is usually finished by the end of the twenty-first day. Although the best time for conception is between the tenth to the fourteenth day, it is still possible up to, and in very rare cases beyond, the twenty-first day.

In the bitch that part of the ovary, the corpus luteum, which produces progesterone, the hormone of pregnancy, continues to function whether or not the bitch is actually pregnant. The body is therefore induced by this hormone to prepare itself for puppies. All bitches are therefore pregnant or false (pseudo) pregnant following every heat. It has become common parlance however to say a bitch has a false pregnancy if she shows unacceptable symptoms such as going off food, occasional vomiting, making beds, digging the garden, cuddling toys, becoming bad tempered and producing milk. Some or all of these symptoms may be present. In most cases treatment is unnecessary but in severe cases hormones may be prescribed by a veterinary surgeon. Symptoms associated with false pregnancy may last several weeks.

Problems associated with female sexuality

1 *Blood* While most bitches clean up the blood produced during the heat, there are some who drip all over floor and furniture.

2 Unwanted attentions of male suitors can be irritating. Much of this is alleviated if the garden is well fenced, but remember a large dog can clear six feet. We have already observed that bitches advertise their condition to local canine hopefuls. The effects of this are considerably reduced if the bitch is kept indoors for the heat period.

3 Inevitably the commonest problem, consequent of a heat, is pregnancy.

Solving the problems of female sexuality

Many people who have never owned a bitch are extremely concerned about the problems of heat. In reality these fears are exaggerated. Sadly some of the animal welfare societies have embarked on widely publicised campaigns to encourage the public to have bitches spayed (removal of the womb and ovaries). These campaigns are hasty, ill considered and of questionable morality. My advice to clients, who seek guidance on the wisdom of spaying their bitch, is 'If you don't have to, don't. Try one heat, see how you get on and make the decision then'.

Spaying

The commonest and most definitive answer to the problems of female sexuality in the dog is neutering (spaying). The operation involves major surgery and during the procedure the womb and ovaries are removed. Following spaying the bitch will not come on heat, cannot conceive, cannot therefore have puppies and cannot have false pregnancies.

Following surgery bitches are likely to feel poorly for two to three days, after which they rapidly recover. It is essential to keep a bitch quiet following surgery. She should be kept off furniture, prevented from climbing stairs and playing, and should not be taken for walks except when essential for elimination processes. At all times outside the house she should be kept on a lead. The wound may be in the mid-line below the umbilicus or on the flank.

Q Does spaying make bitches fat?

A This is a vexed question. Many spayed bitches become fat but then so do many unspayed bitches. (See Obesity) There may be a tendency for the spayed bitch to put on weight more easily than an unspayed bitch but this can easily be overcome with a controlled diet.

Q Does spaying alter the dog's temperament?

A There is no evidence that it does, indeed there is considerable evidence that it does not. All guide dogs for the blind are spayed, as are some police dogs. In neither case does the operation alter or interfere with their ability to work effectively. My own observations both on patients and on one of my bitches spayed for medical reasons confirm that there is no detectable change of temperament.

Tying tubes

This operation commonly performed in women is rarely undertaken in bitches. Simply tying the tubes will prevent pregnancy but will not prevent the sexual cycle nor the associated problems of closely attendant amorous males.

The Pill

In recent years, not to be outdone by medical colleagues, veterinary surgeons can offer the contraceptive Pill to their canine patients. This is a viable alternative to spaying. A calculated dose based on the weight of the bitch is given at the first sign of blood appearing from the vulva. The dose is given daily for eight consecutive days. This will suppress all signs of heat in a very few days. Male dogs fail to show interest and the bitch will not develop an inclination to mate. In most cases the bitch will not come on heat again for about five months when the Pill can be repeated.

The Pill is particularly useful if a bitch is required for breeding. She can be given the Pill for each heat she is not to be mated but be allowed a normal heat, mating and pregnancy when a litter is wanted.

Many owners who normally manage their bitch quite adequately when she is on heat without the aid of modern veterinary science may seek assistance if for example they calculate that their bitch is due on heat during an annual holiday. By adjusting the dose of the Pill the onset of heat can be postponed.

Q Does the dog Pill have any long-term effects?

A Veterinary opinion is divided on this subject. I have not myself seen any evidence of adverse effects but I know veterinary surgeons who feel that they have. I do however question the general principle of juggling with the complex balance of hormones in the body. As with the use of the Pill in human social medicine the advantages must be weighed against the disadvantages.

Contraceptive injections

Contraceptive injections have been available for several years. One injection is required every six months. I have considerable reservation about this method. The makers list so many contra-indications for their use that one is inclined to hesitancy. In addition personal clinical experience has cast so many doubts that I prefer not to use them.

Mis-mating (misalliance)

The long stop of contraception is the injection which can be administered following an unwanted mating. If you choose to allow your bitch to have natural heats but by some mischance she is mated, it is possible to have an injection preferably within twenty-four hours of the event which will prevent conception. The injection prolongs the heat by several days. Unfortunately the injection is not without its risks – it can precipitate a womb infection – and should be used sparingly and only as a last resort. I advise owners to let the bitch have pups if at all possible in preference to the injection.

Menopause

Bitches do not undergo true menopause. The heats may become less regular with age or less apparent but they do not stop altogether as the menstrual cycle does in the human female.

Canine sexuality – male

The male dog is sexually stimulated by the presence of a bitch on heat. Domestic male dogs allowed their freedom are ardent in the pursuit of a receptive female, spending long watchful hours guarding her abode. At the peak of her receptivity they will scale high walls in an attempt to achieve their objective.

Domestic male dogs restricted to the home will often show behavioural changes if a bitch is on heat nearby. They detect her presence largely by smell. Such dogs may stop eating, cry and whimper and show aggressive change in character.

Solving the problems of male sexuality

There are only two ways of reducing the sex drive of the male dog. One method is to administer female sex hormones, so called chemical castration. This alters the balance of the hormones in the body and effectually reduces the dog's maleness.

The more common method is to remove the centres of male hormone production, the testicles, completely. The operation, castration, is relatively simple and carries little surgical risk.

The castration of a male dog is however to be deplored. While spaying of bitches is of questionable morality, the castration of male dogs is an abomination. This opinion is not based on male chauvinism, but on an understanding of the hormone status of both sexes. To a large extent the female temperament remains on a constant plane throughout the year except for the two periods of ovarian activity

A litter at home is the best biology lesson for children

when she is on heat. During the heat period there is a marked change of behaviour and temperament. The removal of a bitch's ovaries ensures that she remains, all through the year, including the time when she is normally on heat, as she is for most of the year before spaying. The only alteration is to prevent two brief periods of changed behaviour. In the male, castration alters the plane of behaviour permanently. He is reduced to a eunuch. Castrated males are flabby, less active, and altogether different beings. Social surgery – operations undertaken for the convenience of the owner not the dog – is always of dubious morality. Castration of male dogs is quite wrong.

The male hormone – testosterone – is, in addition to its obvious sexual connection, associated with territorial behaviour and above all aggression. In practice castration is as often undertaken to reduce these two effects as to negate the dog's sexuality. Castrated dogs are less inclined to wander and are generally much less aggressive. The results of surgical castration are not consistent and the dog which is operated upon because it attacks members of the family may well continue this unacceptable behaviour after surgery. Many owners however prefer to try castration in preference to euthanasia.

Vasectomy

This operation prevents sperm leaving the testicle. It does not stop the dog's sexuality and it does not reduce the urge or the ability to mate. It has absolutely no effect on the production of the male hormone and therefore in no way makes the dog less male. It will not stop wandering and does not reduce aggression.

Since castration is rarely undertaken to prevent mating but usually to prevent wandering or aggression the operation of vasectomy is of limited use in veterinary medicine.

Q How do I find a mate for my male dog?

A Almost impossible unless you know a friend who wants to let you try your dog with their bitch. To be used as a stud a male has to have achieved an enviable record in the show ring.

Q How do I stop a dog performing sexual thrusts on cushions or on children?

A Stop it when young. Most adolescent male dogs develop this habit. They will stop if told. They should be stopped since male dogs riding children become excited and if the child attempts to push them away they may get aggressive and bite.

Q Does it help to let a dog mate a bitch?

A A strange question which veterinary surgeons are often asked. One mating does not reduce human desire, why ever should it reduce a dog's?

Breeding

Before deciding to allow your bitch to have a litter of puppies reflect a while upon the demands it will make on you. The once-off home bred litter is demanding of time and space. Feeding a litter, particularly of the larger breeds, from weaning to selling can be an expensive business which the sale of pups will do but little to refurbish. You can be sure that you will not make a fortune.

But breeding can be fun. It is rewarding. The bitch may enjoy it and your children will have a practical lesson of unparalleled poignancy in biology.

Natural pairing and mating

It is worth reflecting briefly on the social and sexual behaviour associated with reproduction in the wolf – the dog's ancestor.

Wolves are thought to pair for life. They therefore live together in close social contact within the security of a pack all through the year. Female wolves have only one heat each year. When the heat starts the male will commence attentions and the intensity of the relationship increases until the time when the bitch is ready to accept mating. Several matings will take place. The pair dig a den in preparation for the litter and they enjoy the support of the rest of the pack at this time.

After the pups are born the mother remains in the den suckling them and keeping them warm. As the pups become more active and weaning takes place she regurgitates food for them on her return from a hunting expedition. Indeed all members of the pack regurgitate food when stimulated to do so by the pups who lick the mouths of their adult pack relatives. Gradually the pups wander farther from the den gaining strength and experience of the outside world until they are old enough and strong enough to accompany the pack which then leaves the vicinity of the breeding den to wander over larger territories.

Recalling that domestication has hardly altered the dog's behaviour at all, we begin to appreciate some of the difficulties we encounter in breeding and rearing domestic dogs.

Preparation for mating

Before you have your bitch mated ensure that she is in good physical condition. She should not be too fat nor too thin. Confirm that she is fully vaccinated and that she has been recently wormed. Both of these procedures must be complete before mating takes place. It is dangerous to do them afterwards, since they may both cause abortion.

Choosing a mate

Unless you have a male dog yourself that you wish to let mate your bitch, you should arrange for a stud dog in plenty of time remembering that ovulation, and therefore the best time for mating, is between 10–14 days. Assuming you have a pedigree bitch, approach a recognised breeder, the names of which can be obtained from the Kennel Club, and arrange to take your bitch to her dog on the appropriate day.

Q How do I know which male dog to use on my bitch?

A The novice would do well to use a dog which is not closely related to the bitch and preferably a dog which has features you feel are lacking in your bitch. If for example your bitch has a head rather longer than is favoured in the breed, choose a dog with a good short head. Breeders are usually willing to assist you in your choice.

Mating

Love in the pedigree dog is not quite the stuff of which romantic novels are made. Remembering our natural behaviour where a pair live together within an organised social society and are well acquainted when the sexual act is contemplated, it is not surprising that a bitch thrust together with a strange dog in strange surroundings is

apprehensive, even aggressive. Neither busy breeders nor dog-owning sons of suburbia have time to waste on canine courtship. If the bitch shows resistance she is trussed, gagged, tied and finally raped by the strange stud.

The actual mating has an unusual feature called the 'tie'. Initially the dog mounts the bitch and using pelvic thrusts introduces his penis into her. After ejaculation the male dog descends from the bitch but is unable – providing a tie has occurred – to withdraw his penis, due to a complicated mechanism characteristic of the dog family. They therefore are forced to stand rump to rump until bitch and dog relax and they can separate. This can take up to half an hour.

Q Is a tie essential for conception?

A No but the chance of conception is increased if a tie occurs.

Problems associated with mating

Having discussed the usual method of putting a bitch to stud it is worth spending a little time discussing problems associated with mating, because they are often raised by clients.

Female wolves do not usually produce their first litter until they are about two years of age. Attempting to mate a bitch too young, before she is emotionally mature, may account for a small percentage of problems.

More commonly problems arise because of the totally unnatural conditions we create for the canine sexual act. To present a maiden bitch to a strange male dog who has never mated before and expect an immediate sexual union is to credit dogs with the archaic Victorian attitudes of basic animal lust. The bitch usually needs to be wooed and the dog encouraged by the bitch for a natural mating to ensue. Since we in our wisdom emphasise the need for the dog to produce sexual speed, a dog trained in the art of male prostitution is essential for success.

One further factor may contribute to an owner's difficulties if they try to mate their bitch with Mr Jones's dog along the road. We have discussed socialisation elsewhere. (See What age should the puppy leave its mother?) If either the bitch or the dog has for any reason been taken from the bitch before the onset of the socialisation period (4–14 weeks) and reared in isolation from dogs it may well not recognise its proposed partner as a potential mate. It will not think of itself as a dog.

Gestation – the period of pregnancy

Gestation lasts sixty-three days on average. It is not unusual however for the pregnancy to finish a few days early or continue a few days longer.

There is no need for any change in the bitch's routine for the first six weeks of pregnancy. Ensure she is fed good quality food, but prevent any tendency to obesity. Fat dogs may have trouble giving birth. Exercise should be maintained at normal levels.

Pregnancy can sometimes be diagnosed at twenty-one days, although with some bitches the diagnosis may have to wait a little longer. In many cases pregnancy is very obvious by six weeks of age. Where there is still doubt and when there is a need for a definite diagnosis X-ray examination can confirm the presence of pups. Their bones are beginning to form at six weeks and will be visible on the X-ray plate. A visit to your veterinary surgeon at this time is useful particularly for the novice breeder.

During the latter part of pregnancy (6–9 weeks) the bitch should be fed half as much again as normal and this should be split into two or three meals rather than the normal one for an adult. The increased size of the puppies in the womb during the last stage of pregnancy makes one large meal rather uncomfortable to consume. A pregnant bitch should be given a good quality diet of varied meats, dog biscuits and a few vegetables. She should also have milk to drink. There is no need to clutter her with added vitamins and minerals unless prescribed by a veterinary surgeon for a specific deficiency problem.

In the later stages of pregnancy exercise should be maintained but long exhausting runs stopped and several shorter walks at a matronly plod substituted. The risk of damaging the pups from outside is small as they are well cushioned in a bag of water. A very severe bang indeed would be required to injure them.

The Thalidomide tragedy has made us only too aware of the dangers associated with drugs administered during pregnancy. Fortunately there are very few indications for drugs during a canine pregnancy. Morning sickness is not a problem and miscarriage is rare in the dog.

Preparing for the birth

Birth is a natural process. Most bitches manage without assistance. In my opinion there is far too much unnecessary interference both by inexperienced owners and by established breeders. Yards of sterilised thread with which to tie the umbilicus, gallons of antiseptic and buckets in which to boil hot water I regard as surplus to requirements. The best advice is to seek the professional help of your veterinary surgeon, if you suspect trouble. There is very little space between a natural birth and the need for professional assistance for the ministrations of the amateur canine midwife.

At least a week before the birth is due prepare a box in which the bitch is to whelp (give birth). In small breeds a large cardboard box is ideal. It is warm, can be replaced if soiled and has plenty of give in the walls to prevent the pups being crushed by the bitch. An alternative is to construct a wooden box with guard rails around the side to prevent crushed pups. Make sure you have plenty of clean newspaper available. This makes a useful warm bedding for whelping and can be easily renewed when soiled. Cellular blankets make the box warm, safe and comfortable.

The whelping box should replace the bitch's own bed. Surroundings with which the bitch is familiar are reassuring, so if for practical reasons it is planned to whelp the bitch in a different room to that in which she normally sleeps make her sleep where the confinement is to take place at least a week before the pups are due. The whelping room should have extra heating available. Young puppies lose body heat very rapidly. They will become cold (hypothermia) and quickly die.

A few things may prove useful at the birth. A pair of stainless steel scissors, washing facilities for yourself, a small cardboard box with a hot water bottle in which to put the puppies if things go wrong and some clean dry towels.

The birth

The bitch will often indicate the onset of whelping – the first stage – with behavioural changes. The bitch may start making beds, and become generally restless. She may pant and look anxious. Very often they refuse food. This stage which starts between 12–24 hours prior to the first straining is often more obvious in a bitch having her first litter.

The second stage begins with the bitch straining. Bitches usually lie down in the whelping box at this time, but first-time whelpers may stand and move in circles or even walk about the room apparently frightened by the process. Some bitches cry, most pant. The first water bag usually appears at the vulva as a sizeable grey balloon. The bitch soon ruptures this by licking. Puppies may come either head or tail first. In those species (dogs, cats, and pigs) which have several young at a time, as many come head as tail first. This is normal. There is therefore no need to feel alarm if the hind feet are presented. Once straining commences the first pup is usually born within half an hour but can be quite normal up to an hour. At birth the umbilical cord remains attached to the placenta but the bitch soon severs it with her teeth. The pup may be born enclosed in the second water bag but this is soon broken by the bitch who licks the pup as soon as it is born.

The third stage, the expulsion of the placenta, usually occurs 10–20 minutes after the birth of the pup. The bitch eats the placenta. With the first pup born the bitch cleans herself at the vulva by licking up the birth fluid, licks the pup and helps the pup find a teat allowing it to suckle. There usually follows a period of rest before straining starts again for the birth of the next pup. This period of rest may be as short as ten minutes or as long as several hours ($\frac{1}{2}$–2 hours is common). The first pup, particularly in a bitch having its first litter, usually requires more effort than those succeeding. Puppies may be born at regular intervals until the whelping is complete or they may come in several batches of two or three in very quick succession with large periods of rest in between.

The placentae may come with the puppy, at regular intervals (10–15 minutes) after the birth of each pup or they may come in irregular batches. On some occasions one or two are retained for several hours following the last pup. I have experienced very few problems associated with retained placentae in the bitch. There is no need to make a fetish of counting them on arrival or to become distressed if they are not seen. Accompanying the birth of pups is a dark green discharge. This is normal. (See What can go wrong)

With all the puppies born, well licked and dry, the bitch settles contentedly to suckle her litter. This is indeed a rewarding sight.

When you are sure the bitch has finished leave her to suckle the pups for about an hour and then it is as well to change the bedding. Remove all soiled newspaper and replace it with clean. It is now safe to add a clean, preferably cellular blanket. This reassures the bitch, makes her comfortable and helps to keep the puppies warm. Thick, non-cellular blankets, if used, should be fixed down to prevent the puppies suffocating.

The role of the owner at whelping

Bitches had their puppies unaided for several million years before they chose to sacrifice their freedom for the comfort of man's hearth. We must not therefore over emphasise our role at a canine confinement. We hope to correct nature's problems and difficulties and make sure that at the conclusion of each birth there is a healthy mother and a litter of live pups. The owner's role is, and should remain, largely passive. The bitch should be left to complete her task by herself. All owners should do is observe, be prepared to assist if there is real trouble and, most important, know when to call for veterinary assistance.

Q Should you be there at all?

A Most family dogs enjoy a close relationship with their owners and their presence at this time often appears to be comforting and reassuring. It is not, however, a viable alternative to poor television. Aunt Flossie, Uncle Tom Cobley and the self-appointed local dog expert should not be invited to fill the stalls. Prepare yourself with as much theoretical knowledge as you can. Most veterinary surgeons are prepared to explain what happens. Remain calm. Don't panic. Reassure the bitch. So long as she is coping adequately with the situation, which, remember, is the case in the vast majority of canine births, talk soothingly to her, offer her the occasional small drink of warm milk but don't fuss, and above all don't interfere. Remember this is an anxious time for the bitch and she needs peace and calm support. She can well do without the assistance of panicky or hysterical owners.

What can go wrong?

This section is prepared for the inexperienced owner and it attempts to indicate stage by stage problems that can go wrong. Remember you are unlikely to see even one of these problems and will certainly not see them all at any single birth. Read it, digest it, but keep it in proportion. Your veterinary surgeon is obviously a key figure. His role is closely associated with this section. I encourage my clients to let me know within reason as soon as the normal birth starts. I can then make sure I am in readiness for any problem that may arise.

A very rare condition, called primary uterine inertia, may occur before you see the bitch straining. This is due to failure of the womb to contract at all. If this is present you may see a dark green discharge BEFORE the birth of the first pup. This certainly means problems and you should consult your veterinary surgeon immediately. Green discharge after the birth of the first pup is of no consequence. It is quite normal.

The firstborn pup of any litter can present problems and it may be particularly difficult for a bitch having her first litter. If she strains for more than an hour without producing the pup call your veterinary surgeon.

Most pups, once they start to emerge, are born within a few minutes. If any pup gets half way out and the bitch cannot complete the expulsion within ten minutes, call your veterinary surgeon.

If the bitch starts a period of straining to produce a pup and does not do so after an hour of effort call your veterinary surgeon.

Inexperienced bitches, particularly with the first pup, may succumb to anxiety and fail to open the second water bag thus preventing the pup from breathing. If this happens simply break the bag with your thumbnail over the puppy's nose, open its mouth and gently rub its head. Bitches with a first litter may also fail to sever the cord. There is no need to worry about this. Indeed if the placenta is expelled before the cord is broken the pup will drag the placenta after it. There is no need to panic, the cord can be cut with sterilised scissors, leaving at least one inch still attached to the pup. This will shrivel in two or three days and disappear.

An inexperienced bitch may appear to panic at the sight and sound of her first pup, and she may keep moving away from it, and may not lick it. Don't worry, that old maternal instinct will almost always overcome her fear and she will soon become attentive, probably after the birth of a few more pups. It may be useful in this case, assuming she has not cleaned the pup or severed the umbilical cord, to do this for her, and to rub the pup in a dry towel. Reasonably vigorous rubbing simulates the mother's licks and helps to stimulate the pup. Once dry and full of wriggle put it back with the bitch.

Some bitches, particularly those who have large litters, may develop secondary uterine inertia, where the womb appears to become too weak to contract with enough vigour to expel the pups. There are several causes for this condition and it needs skilled attention. If the bitch therefore seems to have only weak straining movements and appears unable to produce puppies you suspect remain unborn, call your veterinary surgeon.

We saw how irregular is the arrival of afterbirth (placenta) in the normal birth. The bitch eats them as a normal function. An odd one can be gobbled very easily while your back is turned so there is no need to worry about the number of afterbirths. Don't bother to count them.

What the veterinary surgeon may do
Unless the problem is obvious the veterinary surgeon will examine the bitch. This will probably include palpation (feeling) of the abdomen to determine the position of the pups. It may also include a vaginal examination to establish the state of the neck of the womb (cervix) and

again the position of the pup and the part, i.e. head or tail, presented. Vaginal palpation is not always possible in small breeds.

If all appears well the veterinary surgeon may decide to simply allow more time, or he may feel one of several injections may be advisable.

The use of forceps in modern canine midwifery is rare. They may, however, be used to grasp a pup just out of reach of fingers, particularly if the pup is thought to be dead.

In general, if the bitch is having real trouble, many veterinary surgeons will prefer to perform a caesarian section to remove the pups, rather than waste a great deal of time hoping for an unlikely improvement in what is probably a rapidly declining situation.

Caesarian section

So called because Julius Caesar is said to have been born as a result of this operation.

The operation requires that the abdominal wall be opened, and the puppies removed through an incision in the womb. Some veterinary surgeons prefer to use a flank incision while others make a mid-line incision running posterior to the umbilicus.

Q Do bitches take to their puppies after the operation?

A It is very rare to have problems. In most cases the puppies will have been returned to the bitch following her recovery from anaesthetic by the veterinary surgeon or the nursing staff. If you are expected to do this yourself wait until the bitch is recovered and keep presenting the pups to her. Stay with her and be vigilant. She may show some initial reluctance but in nearly all cases your patience will be rewarded with a contented family scene.

Q Do I need to feed the puppies?

A No. It will not hurt the pups to wait for the mother to recover and accept them. If you feed them artificially you are more likely to create problems than solve them.

Q Can bitches which have had a caesarian section have further litters?

A Yes. There is absolutely no medical reason to prevent more litters. Many breeders don't favour breeding from these bitches again, because the operation frequently needs to be repeated. Indeed some veterinary surgeons believe one should always perform a caesarian section for each subsequent litter. In practice further litters may well be born without trouble although the risk is slightly increased.

Stages of normal puppy development – the period of lactation

With the birth now over the mother will settle down to care for her puppies. Soon after birth the puppies begin to move forward with their head swaying from side to side only to stop when they meet the warm furry body of their mother. They seek and quickly find a teat and are very soon suckling. The mother's duties at this time are of course principally to provide adequate supplies of liquid refreshment. In addition she keeps the puppies warm, cuddling them in close to her. Two further important duties are keeping the puppies clean and, even more vital, stimulating their bowels and bladders to evacuate. Both of the latter tasks she achieves with her tongue. Licking the rear end is essential. Puppies cannot pass faeces or urine unless so stimulated for the first few days of life.

For the first 24–48 hours following the birth most bitches are diligently protective. They are extremely reluctant to leave the puppies even to pass urine or to eat. You should encourage the bitch to eat and drink, offering it to her in her bed if necessary. She should be taken out to pass urine but under no circumstances should she be kept from the puppies for more than the briefest period. Enthusiasm gradually wanes until by six weeks most bitches spend only brief periods with their pups. Contented thriving puppies do not cry for long periods. Excessive persistent crying is a sign of problems. Consult your veterinary surgeon urgently.

The puppies' eyes and ears remain closed for the first ten days of life during which time they eat, sleep and are licked.

Following the opening of their eyes the puppies' awareness of their environment begins to develop. The elements of play are seen. Their movements begin to change from squirming to walking. By the time they are weaned at about 4–5 weeks they are running around.

Natural weaning among wolves and other wild dogs occurs when the mother, and indeed other adult members of the pack, regurgitate food for the puppies to eat. Many domestic bitches retain this pattern and will regurgitate food when their puppies lick their mouths.

Domestic puppies are very easy to wean. A plate of porridge or other cereal, made with milk (some of the balanced baby cereals are excellent) and placed in an open dish is readily accepted. If there is any reluctance puppies will soon learn to lick the porridge off your finger and having got the taste will soon learn to lap it up. Start feeding with one or two small meals of cereal and gradually build up. Eventually by 6–8 weeks they should be having four meals each day. Two should be of meat (fresh meat, not tinned or synthetic) together with wholemeal tread or commercial puppy biscuit, and two of cereal made with milk. The meat should be introduced gradually. I do not favour giving synthetic 'all in one' foods for puppies and I do not approve of tinned

For the first few weeks of life, the puppies contentedly suckle and sleep

or other commercially available meat or meat substitutes. In my opinion, based on the observation of many puppies from a wide variety of venues, fresh meat, wholemeal bread or puppy biscuit meal, milk and cereal are the best foods and they will give your puppies the best start. (See also Feeding)

Q Does the bitch stop producing milk when the pups are weaned?
A Not abruptly. It is a gradual process.
Q Should she have anything to stop the milk?
A No. Emphatically no! As the demand decreases so does the supply.

Problems which may affect the bitch while she is nursing the pups
As soon as whelping is complete the bitch settles down. The puppies suckle at regular intervals and sleep for most of the remaining time. The bitch will eat and drink but may, as we have seen, be reluctant to leave her pups. Any deviation from this situation should be viewed with suspicion, and veterinary assistance be recruited.

Bitches which have problems with their litter, i.e. when the pups keep crying or when because of anxiety she becomes distressed, may indulge in the doggy equivalent of baby battering – she may kill her pups.

1 Some bitches show symptoms of disease following the birth. They may refuse food, vomit, appear lethargic and the puppies may cry a great deal due to lack of milk. Fever at this time may be due to a retained placenta or a general infection.

2 Eclampsia

Also called milk fever and puerperal tetany. This condition is due to a low blood calcium, and it can occur from any time just before birth until the end of lactation although it is most common during the first two weeks after the birth of the pups. In the early stages the bitch pants and becomes excited, nervous and restless. She begins to be unsteady on her feet, breathing rapidly and whining. The body temperature can be extremely high. After a variable period the affected bitch falls to the ground panting, has glazed eyes and, with legs outstretched, trembles. It closely resembles a fit to the inexperienced eye. While lying on her side the bitch may have convulsions. There may be salivation. Immediate treatment by a veterinary surgeon is essential if the bitch's life is to be saved. The treatment is intravenous injection of soluble calcium.

Bitches once afflicted with eclampsia are likely to suffer recurrent attacks both during the same and subsequent lactations. The wisdom of breeding from these bitches must be assessed. Following an attack the puppies should be removed for several hours and they should be weaned as soon as possible.

The condition is due to a low circulating blood calcium. Although the body has a massive store of calcium in the bones, bitches which suffer from eclampsia appear to have difficulty in mobilising the reserve. The sudden insistent demand by the milk producing organs – the mammary glands – for calcium leaves the blood temporarily short and it is this which causes the trouble. Preventative measures include adding calcium, in readily absorbent form, to the food and in some cases injections of calcium prior to whelping and during lactation. In spite of such precautions however susceptible bitches may still succumb.

Q Will the bitch have eclampsia every time she has puppies?

A She very likely will. To some extent the condition can be prevented by feeding a quantity of calcium all through pregnancy, but even this is no guarantee of success.

Q Should the puppies be weaned?

A Rearing young puppies by hand is a very difficult and time consuming occupation. It is better to let the bitch do the job for which she is suited. However if she has repeated bouts, it is as well to wean the pups as early as possible (3 weeks).

3 Mastitis (inflammation of the mammary glands or teats)

Inflammation with or without concurrent infection is a painful and serious condition which occasionally affects a lactating bitch. One or more of the teats may become hot, swollen, red and painful if touched. The bitch is naturally reluctant to let the puppies feed and they, being therefore very hungry begin to cry more than usual. Veterinary attention is essential.

4 In later lactation as the puppies grow and their teeth and claws become needle sharp their relentless devotion to their mother's teats begins to become a burden. The teats become scratched, bitten and sore. The bitch will show considerable reluctance to let the pups suckle, or let them suckle briefly with her in the standing position. At this stage the teats should be kept clean with warm water and the pups weaned.

5 Bitches with large litters tend to lose condition if food intake has been poor in quality or quantity. If you think she is beginning to lose condition increase the quantity of food and start to wean the pups or increase their food if already weaned to relieve the burden on her.

Problems affecting the puppies after birth and within the first few weeks of life

We have seen that soon after the birth of the litter is complete the bitch and the puppies settle to a contented life of suckling and sleeping. The puppies should be examined soon after birth. Healthy puppies are warm, round, soft objects which move with a strong squirming movement. They suckle with enthusiasm.

Poor unhealthy puppies may be thin, weak and often feel cold. They move around a great deal, often rather feebly and may cry for long periods.

1 Soon after birth puppies can be examined for abnormality. They may have cleft palates and hair lips, the former often evidenced by difficulty in suckling and frothy milk coming down their nose. These conditions can be surgically repaired, but as cleft palates and hair lips are inherent, dogs thus inflicted must not be used for breeding.

2 Poor puppies, so-called runts, of which there is commonly although not invariably one or even two in the litter, should be carefully examined and their chance of survival assessed. If they are very weak and poor in condition humane euthanasia should be considered. This is preferable to a few days or weeks of struggle with death as a result. If the runt seems capable of survival supplementary feeding should be considered. Take your veterinary surgeon's opinion before making a decision.

3 Abnormal limbs should be examined and professional assistance

sought. Many quite bizarre limb abnormalities will rectify themselves given time or with the assistance of simple treatment.

4 Hernias are not unusual in puppies, the commonest being in the middle of the abdomen – the umbilical hernia – where the umbilical cord was attached to the placenta in the womb. Many of these are small and do not require treatment, while others are very large and will require surgical correction. It is always as well to seek the advice of your veterinary surgeon if you suspect an umbilical hernia.

Other types of hernia of the new born include inguinal in the groin and much more rarely diaphragmatic which cannot be seen but may cause problems with breathing. (See Part III, Hernias)

5 If the bitch is ill following the birth for reasons already discussed she may fail to produce sufficient milk, or in rare cases produce infected or poor quality milk. In this case the pups will cry a great deal. The bitch needs treatment.

6 Individual puppies or whole litters may become infected through the opening at the umbilicus.

7 The fading puppy syndrome is a well recognised and serious problem in which the whole litter may show illness and may die. This is a very complex condition with many, many causes. At the first suggestion of a problem you should seek veterinary advice.

8 When the eyes begin to open, between 10–12 days, it is not uncommon for one or two puppies to have one or both of their eyes gummed, and for them not to open. If simple bathing with cold boiled water does not release them, seek veterinary advice. If on opening them you see yellow pus in the eye you should consult your veterinary surgeon.

9 The Foramen Fontanelle, the hole in the bones at the top of the head is present in the developing dog. As with children it normally closes. The hole – Foramen Fontanelle – remains throughout life in the chihuahua, being quite normal for that breed. In the Yorkshire terrier it fails to close in a few individuals and is abnormal.

Tail docking

A brief note on the vexed question of tail docking. I believe this is a totally unnecessary and quite unjustifiable abuse of the dog. It has absolutely no function at all and is purely performed in the interest of fashion. It must surely soon become illegal. Already the practice is condemned by the veterinary profession. If a concerted campaign by the reasonable majority of society could be organised this mindless mutilation would rapidly be outlawed.

Arguments in its favour are fatuous, those who support docking

White boxer pup. Fashion dictates that these are destroyed at birth. This lucky one survives, due to the rational thinking of its owner.

claim for example that spaniels with long tails get them torn while out working. This is rubbish. If the undergrowth through which the dogs worked were such that skin was torn by it then a great deal more of the dog's body, all the bit before the tail, would surely be lacerated as well. Setters and English pointers are not docked, while German short haired pointers are. Labrador retrievers are not docked while weimaraners are. Irrefutable evidence is there for those who have the eyes to see. A few enlightened breeders of dogs normally docked are now refusing to mutilate their puppies. Power to their elbow.

There are however difficulties for the owner who has a litter of pedigree puppies which normally carry docked tails. Since law does not prohibit this practice and since they will find it very difficult, if not impossible, to sell them unless they are docked, owners are left with little real alternative.

Veterinary surgeons are now in an invidious position. The practice is condemned by the Royal College of Veterinary Surgeons, and by the majority of veterinary surgeons themselves, but if we are to offer a complete service to clients and if we are to prevent back street dockers mutilating puppies I feel we should continue to dock, indicating at the same time our disgust to clients. Clear thinking people should press for prohibitive legislation.

Removal of dew claws

The argument for the removal of dew claws is more complex than for tail docking. The front dew claws should not be removed. They invariably have good functional articulation with the foot. Most puppies are born without hind dew claws. Some however do have vestigial claws when born. They often have no boney attachment to the foot being just a flap of skin with a free bone inside and a claw on the end. In adult life the claw does tend to catch on objects and since it does not function correctly, often grows long and needs to be manicured. Contrarily some breed standards – for example the Pyrennean mountain dog – insist that the hind dew claws are retained.

To sum up it would seem the hind dew claw has little function being a vestigial organ in the process of becoming an evolutionary memory. Since most puppies are born without them there is no argument for their retention and since they can be a nuisance in adult life it would seem sensible to remove them at 4–5 days of age.

Feeding orphan puppies

Occasionally a bitch dies at birth either as a result of infection or following caesarian section. Some bitches may have infected or in-adequate milk. It may be considered that the litter is too large for the bitch to feed adequately, and to reduce her burden hand rearing is advised.

Whatever the reason, hand rearing puppies is not to be undertaken casually. It is a demanding and time consuming activity, and unless you are certain you have the ability to devote yourself to the task unstintingly then you would be wiser not to begin and to leave it to someone free of commitment.

Orphan puppies must be kept warm and clean and they must be fed. They are best kept in an insulated box – a cardboard box wrapped in a blanket is excellent – which is capable of being kept at quite high temperatures. For the first week of life puppies should be kept at 85 °F. From then until weaning the temperature can be reduced to between 75 °–80 °F. These temperatures are very important since small puppies lose heat very quickly, become hypothermic, and can die. Warm pieces of blanket over newspaper make excellent beds. Cellular blankets are best. Ideally heating can be supplied by an infra-red lamp, or by one of the commercially available heating pads, but any method is acceptable so long as it is constant.

It has been suggested that orphan puppies should be isolated until they are about five weeks of age. This prevents the puppies sucking each other, a habit which develops due to deprivation of normal sucking behaviour. While the sucking, which often concentrates on the genitalia, is a problem, the psychological and social difficulties created for the puppies by keeping them isolated for the first five critical weeks are legion. Isolation is not justified.

Feeding puppies initially presents a few problems. Cows' milk is, on its own, no substitute for bitches' milk as it has too little fat and has too much milk sugar (lactose). It causes diarrhoea, which in turn causes dehydration (loss of body fluid) and death. Substitutes for bitches' milk are commercially available. Your veterinary surgeon will advise you. For those scientifically minded who wish to prepare their own bitch milk substitute, the following formula can be used:

800 ml of cows' milk; 200 ml of cream to increase the fat;
the yolk of an egg; 5 gms of sterile bone meal;
2,000 units of Vitamin A; 500 units of Vitamin D.
This should be blended and 4 gms of citric acid added.

This milk substitute should be prepared with scrupulous attention to sterility as for a human baby and should be at body temperature when fed. The puppies of small breeds should be fed with an eye dropper, or small dolls' feeding bottle. Large pups can be fed with a premature baby bottle readily available from chemists or with commercially available puppy rearing bottles. The holes in the rubber teats need to be larger than for a human baby and should therefore be enlarged. Never force feed puppies.

During the first week of life orphaned pups should be fed on demand, which in practice is about every two hours and at this critical stage it is advisable to feed at least two meals during the night. Be sure to keep the bottle properly tilted to prevent pups sucking in air. With the first week negotiated successfully the night feeds can be reduced or stopped but feeding should go on until as late as possible in the evening and start again early in the morning. It is impossible to be definitive about quantities, but puppies can be allowed to suck at each feed until they seem to be satisfied. Remember puppies which continually cry may be underfed. Those with diarrhoea may be underfed, being fed an incorrect diet or may have an infection. If in any doubt consult your veterinary surgeon.

By the time puppies are three weeks of age you can begin weaning. Remember however that bottle feeding should continue, gradually reducing the frequency and quantity until the puppies are fully weaned.

As we have seen, defaecation and urination are normally stimulated during the first few days of life by the bitch licking the puppies' anus and genitalia (perineum) and the abdomen. Orphaned puppies must have a substitute bitch's tongue to provide this stimulus or they will not be able to pass faeces or urine. A warm wet piece of cotton wool rubbed gently over these vital parts is ideal and also helps to keep puppies clean. Each pup should be rubbed in this manner after every feed and it should be continued until elimination has taken place.

The importance of sterility and cleanliness in the care and preparation of food has already been emphasised. It is especially important to keep the pups clean. Frequent changes of blankets and diligent removal of faeces when the pups get older will keep them wholesome.

Genetics

Genetics is the study of inherited characters, the way in which parental features are passed to their offspring. The subject, first studied by the Russian monk Mendel, is now an important and complex branch of biology. Space does not allow the subject to be discussed in depth but an example of simple mendelian inheritance will introduce the subject for the novice and may stimulate the scientifically minded to delve a little deeper into a fascinating subject.

Characters – colour of eyes, colour of skin, blood group, long, short

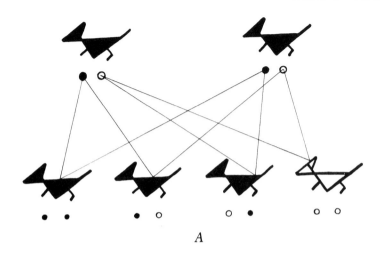

A

or wire coat, prick or flop ears – are all carried as chemical instructions, each of which is called a gene, joined together as strings of complex chemical proteins called chromosomes. Each chromosome is composed of one set of instructions from the father, carried in the sperm, and another set from the mother's egg.

We can take a simple hypothetical example. If in a breed of dog the colour were to be for simplicity only either black or white, one of these colours will be dominant. Let us assume it is black. Now each dog, male or female, will have instructions from both its mother and its father. Let us assume two dogs, one male and one female, each have the black instructions from one of their parents and the white instructions from the other. Since the black instruction is dominant both dog and bitch will be black.

Now half of the sperms will carry the instruction for black and half for white. Similarly half of the eggs will carry black character instruction and half white. If we look at diagram A we see how these will combine. A black sperm from the male may fertilise either a black or a white egg. The white sperm may also fertilise either a black or white egg, and the resulting puppies will be born in the proportions shown. One quarter will carry only black instructions, these pups will be black. One half will have both black and white instructions, but because black is dominant these pups will be black and indistinguishable to look at from the puppies with all black instructions. One quarter will have only white instructions and therefore, with no black instructions to override them the puppies will be white.

If one parent with only black instructions is mated to a parent with only white, then the first generation will all have mixed instructions, but will all have black coats (see diagram B), since black is dominant. The second generation will however be in the proportion described above – one pure black, two mixed black and white but looking black, and one white.

If for any reason, such as unpopularity of one or other of the two colours in the show ring, we wish to concentrate on breeding only one of the colours, we would want to produce from parents who had carried only the single colour instructions. It is important to realise that these diagrams represent proportions, i.e. they hold over several hundred random combinations of sperm and egg. They do not hold for every four puppies born.

If we are trying to identify breeding animals carrying only black or white instruction, it is necessary to make a careful study of pedigrees, constantly working our inheritance diagrams backwards rather than forwards as we have done above, because only by this method can identify pure colour parents.

Breeders, particularly of the food animals, cattle, pigs, sheep and poultry, use very sophisticated techniques to fix characters which will improve production. Inherited conditions are also studied and

B

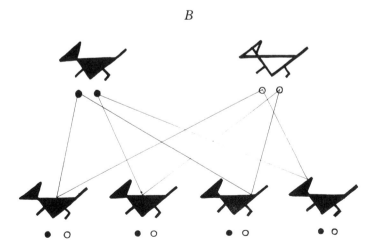

attempts made to breed these diseases out of the stock. There are a few examples in the dog world where the science of genetics has been employed in attempts to breed out inherited diseases. The two best known examples, the hip dysplasia scheme and the progressive retinal atrophy scheme, both supported jointly by the British Veterinary Association and the Kennel Club, have had only limited success. The reasons for this are complex but are due in part to those diseases being controlled, not by a single instruction like our hypothetical example, but by several genes making eradication extremely difficult.

Showing
Conformation

As previously discussed I have serious moral and ethical reservations about showing dogs. My interest and delight in dogs is in their natural history, their personality, and their social behaviour. Showing, which concentrates on the superficial structure, the packaging, the tinsel and pretty ribbon, seems to me to concentrate on the least important aspect of dogs. While one cannot but admire the vital statistics of the contenders for Miss World, few of us would deny that there is a great deal more to an attractive lady companion.

It cannot be denied that a great many people derive considerable pleasure from pitting the physical attributes of their polished and powdered pooches against others of their kind, to be judged by another human being whose arbitrary assessment is based on no more than personal preference and current fashion. So be it.

For those owners whose pedigree dogs are registered with the Kennel Club and who wish to join the show ring circus, enrolment with the breed society for their breed is an advisable first step. They will then receive information about shows. Before entering your dog in a show it is wise to contact a breeder interested in your breed. Breeders are usually willing to help you on the first few rungs of the ladder and they will advise you about ring training and general preparation of the dog for the show, and how to enter.

Do not be disappointed if you do not get the champion award first time. Try several shows and ask each judge afterwards why your dog was placed as it was. Different judges favour various characteristics within a breed. Part of the art of showing is to put your dog under a judge which favours your type. Judges are usually helpful, particularly to a novice. They will often point out the faults of your dog and its strong features. Only if you meet with consistent failure under several judges should you retire gracefully or, if your enthusiasm for this pastime is not totally eroded, consider buying another puppy, this time, perhaps, from a well-established and successful breeder.

I am told that the supreme thrill is experienced when a dog of one's own breeding achieves high accolade in the ring.

Dog shows started in the first half of the nineteenth century. One of the most popular sites was the Crystal Palace, the home of the Great Exhibition of 1851, and moved from Hyde Park to South London. The Kennel Club, formed by the National Dog Club in 1873 became the governing body of pedigree dog fancy in the United Kingdom.

To-day dog shows are classed as 'open' in which all comers compete or 'members' to which only members of the society running the show are permitted. Various types of show are held. Some are restricted to one breed, others to a few specified breeds or group of breeds, others cater for all breeds. Championship shows are those which award the coveted Challenge Certificates of the Kennel Club. The Kennel Club runs a graded scheme which essentially gives beginners and novice dogs a chance to show what they are made of without the aggressive presence of high class dogs. Thus the more classes a dog wins the fewer are the classes for which it is eligible. This ensures that each dog is continually placed against tougher and tougher opposition and cannot loaf around content to mop up the low grade prizes.

Obedience shows

Obedience trials are a newer innovation than conformation shows. They developed after the First World War. From very early, critics of the dog show wanted some form of intelligence test included to prove that beauty was more than skin deep. Sadly the marriage of these two divisions of the dog fancy has never been consummated. It is indeed rare to find a dog successful in both spheres.

Between thirty and forty obedience championship shows are held each year. In addition there are several hundred obedience trials which award no title honours. Similar to conformation shows, Obedience Champion (Ob.Ch.) is awarded to a dog which wins three certificates under different judges.

Like the conformation shows obedience competition is graded so that a newcomer starts competing in novice classes and gradually, as the dog improves, moves to compete against fiercer opposition.

Field trials

Field trials recognised by the Kennel Club are divided into three main sections. 1 Pointers and Setters 2 Retrievers 3 Spaniels. Each trial takes place in the field using free living game, under conditions appropriate for the breed of dog competing. Each section runs its own trials according to Kennel Club rules.

1 *Pointers and Setters*   The function of these breeds is to locate the game by its scent and then to move slowly in the characteristic stance of the breed, pointing the game to the gun. When the birds take off, the dog drops to the ground to keep out of the line of fire. Pointers and setters do not retrieve. For this reason killing birds is not essential in their trials, and these can therefore take place outside the shooting season, blank shot being used. The trials are divided into puppy, novice, and open classes.

In these trials, pairs of dogs competing are selected by ballot, each one of the pair belonging to different owners. The dogs are then released, one quartering the ground to the left, the other to the right. They run in great sweeps, moving slowly forward followed by their handlers, the guns and the judges. When one dog scents game it freezes, pointing. The handler and gun move forward. The second dog on seeing the first dog on point stops and points the first dog. When the bird takes wing the shot is fired and the dogs are set to beat again. After each pair has had two attempts at birds the judges decide who should go forward to the next round. The whole procedure is repeated until a winner emerges.

2 *Retrievers*   Retriever trials are always held in the shooting season. Wild game are shot over natural ground. The trials are divided into puppy, novice and open classes. Basically the dogs are lined up and as the birds are shot the handlers are invited at the request of the judges to send them to retrieve. Points are awarded for the care with which the bird is retrieved, the speed it is returned and the pass to the handler. Each dog is run under two different judges who, after consultation, decide which dog they would like to see run again. Eventually by elimination they select the winner.

3 *Spaniels*   Spaniels are the rough shooters, Jack of all trades. No disdainful glance of the plummeting bird for them. They have to work close to their handler, find and flush fur and feather, and then retrieve the game that is shot. Two dogs are worked at trials. Two judges used. The spaniel must not be so keen that it 'runs in', and the game must be mouthed tenderly.

The coveted award for gun dogs is Field Trial Champion (F.T.Ch.).

4 *Sheepdog trials*   Sheepdog trials first started in Wales in 1873. Since the early 1920s national trials have been held in England,

The author's son with his English pointer Trottwood.

Scotland and Wales. Top dogs from each trial progress to the international trial for that year. Sheepdog trials test the ability of the dog to do its job under simulated working conditions. Most competing dogs regularly work sheep on hill farms. Border collies are used for sheepdog trials and competing dogs are entered in the stud book of the International Sheepdog Society.

Travelling with dogs
By car

Since so much of our lives is woven around the motor car, dogs not at home in them are something of a nuisance to their owners. Puppies should be trained to go in the car from the start. The car must become an extension of your home, part of the territory the dog expects to cherish and defend. Although puppies must not walk the streets before the vaccination programme is complete there is absolutely no reason why you should not take your puppy for rides in the car. The earlier he is introduced to it, the sooner will he become accustomed to and accept it. Very short rides frequently throughout the day will acclimatise most puppies. They soon accept car travel as a normal part of the daily routine. Any puppy which continues to show hesitation or reluctance may improve if you sit with it in the car while it is stationary in your garage or garden. Continued reserve may well be overcome finally by feeding the puppy once or twice each day in the car.

A few dogs have problems with car travel in spite of diligent training. Others, because of poor training as puppies, never become relaxed and familiar with the pleasures associated with car rides. There are four common, basic problems; dogs which are hysterical, crying and even leaping about, dogs which never overcome their fear and which try to hide under seats, dogs which salivate to the disgust of their owner and detriment of the upholstery, and finally dogs which vomit. Fortunately all of these problems can be alleviated by behavioural retraining or with appropriate medication, so consult your veterinary surgeon. (See Part I, Behavioural problems)

By train and boat

Dogs which are to travel frequently by these modes of transport are few. Sensible dogs which enjoy a good relationship with their owner, based on mutual trust and respect, will usually accompany their owner anywhere without hesitation so long as the owner appears confident. Dogs which do not fit this description should be crated if such a journey is unavoidable. Tranquillisation can be used – consult your veterinary surgeon.

By aeroplane

International regulations dictate that dogs be carried in crates of quite specific size and design. The measurement of the crate depends on the size of the dog. There are several firms who specialise in making these crates although airlines often provide the crates themselves. If you anticipate sending your dog by air, allow plenty of time prior to travelling for preparation and documentation and consult the airline for details. (See Export of dogs) Tranquillisation prior to air travel is a controversial question. Most airlines and professional dog shippers prefer not to tranquillise. This I understand is related to legal action in the event of the dog's death during transportation. Personally I see no objection to tranquillisation. I have been responsible for sending numerous dogs by air, and have usually administered tranquillisers without any ill effects, in the knowledge that much of the dogs' inevitable anxiety is alleviated.

Boarding kennels

Dogs are adaptable. They are social animals, as we have seen, with a strong sense of attachment to the members of their pack. It is, then, a little surprising that incarceration in unfamiliar surroundings among strange people and unknown dogs is accepted by the vast majority so easily. It is surprising but it is true. Of course it would be better if you didn't have to leave them, it is more fun for them if you can take them away with you but this is not always possible. Holidays abroad are out of the question for dogs, even in our affluent society, because of the quarantine regulations on their return.

Choose a boarding kennel carefully. Give yourself plenty of time and book early because they become very full in the holiday period and those who leave selection to the last minute may well have no choice at all, being forced to take what they can get. Do not accept the word or recommendation of a friend. Be sure that you are yourself satisfied. Contact the proprietor and arrange to visit the kennels before you make a booking. I believe you should be allowed to see over a kennel without prior warning of your visit, but be reasonable. Do not go early in the morning before the dogs' cleaning and feeding can possibly have been completed – you would not like your house inspected by a critical eye before the vacuum cleaner had done its work – and do not expect to call at weekends. I would strongly suggest you reject any kennel that refuses you entry. A good kennel has nothing to hide.

For those who are unfamiliar with kennels, assessment of their worth can be difficult. The proprietor is an important factor. Attitudes stem from the top. The staff should be helpful, sensibly but smartly attired and appear to enjoy their work. Morose, sullen girls with the all too familiar couldn't-care-less attitude are not the sort to look after your dog.

The kennels themselves may vary considerably in their structure. They should be bright, easy to clean and seen to be kept clean. Dogs should have an exercise area attached to their sleeping quarters or, if separate, into which they are put each day. One has to take the latter arrangement on trust. The dogs should appear well groomed and the majority – you get the odd sulker anywhere – should advance to see you full of bounce and bark. Each dog should have a sleeping bench raised from the floor.

Good kennels insist that vaccination certificates are up to date. Indeed if they do not so insist one is well advised to reject the kennels, for it suggests a sloppy and unforgivable attitude to disease control and this may well extend to other areas of canine health.

Finally a word in defence of those gallant souls who run boarding kennels. It is often a thankless task. The dogs don't want to be there, the owners don't want to leave them and certainly are not amused to pay the account. With so many dogs congregated together the risk of infection is high. One dog has only to come in incubating, but not showing symptoms of, an infectious disease and the proprietors are faced with a horrifying problem. By all means be critical of the service offered but do not demand perfection.

Import of dogs to the U.K.

Dogs imported into the United Kingdom have to undergo a period of quarantine for six months. There is no argument that this regulation causes distress to owners and discomfort to the incarcerated dog. It is totally justified, however, in our attempt to keep rabies, one of the most horrible diseases known, from our shores. Anybody who, from a misguided affection for their pet, tries to circumnavigate this requirement by smuggling a dog into the country would do well to contemplate the consequences of their action if their pet were to introduce this dreaded disease to our island. They might also like to consider their betrayal of all the thousands of dogs and owners who comply with the regulation. Their discomfort and deprivation will have been for nothing if the selfish stupidity of one owner denies them their self sacrifice.

Dogs entering the country must have prior permission to do so.

This can be obtained by writing to the Ministry of Agriculture, State Veterinary Service, Import of Dogs and Cats, Hook Rise South, Tolworth, Surbiton, Surrey, or telephoning 01-337-6611.

Dogs are collected from the port or airport of entry by a licensed carrier and taken by them in the travelling case in which they arrive to the quarantine kennels of your choice, which should also have been pre-arranged. During the quarantine period the dogs will be subjected to supervision by a veterinary surgeon, and will be vaccinated against rabies. Owners are allowed to visit their dogs frequently.

Q Is the personality of dogs changed by six months' quarantine?

A Most dogs show little effect, especially if owners are able to visit them frequently. Some dogs of an excitable disposition do appear hyperactive, but they inevitably settle down within a few days of release. Occasionally dogs appear to become depressed by their captivity but again this is short lived and when they have served their term and rejoined their owners, normal behaviour patterns return.

Export of dogs

Taking or exporting dogs from the U.K. is fraught with the frustration which inevitably accompanies international bureaurocracy. Each country has its own idiosyncrasies, its own regulations with which to confound and confuse the innocence and naïvety of the traveller. Some countries demand rabies vaccination, others want bilingual health certificates, a number demand an export certificate from the Ministry of Agriculture stating that there have been no outbreaks of rabies for a period of time, a few demand blood tests for obscure diseases and one or two insist on specific wording on the certificates. The variation in the time for issue of a health certificate before the dog travels is bewildering. Add to this the complication of ever-changing regulations and you see you can be in for real problems.

Where can you go for advice? The airlines, or rather their employees, I know from personal experience may misread, mistake or misinterpret the regulations and cause you endless heartache. Foreign embassies are even worse. There is no doubt the best and most up to date advice about the export of dogs to all foreign countries can be obtained from our own Ministry of Agriculture, and anyone contemplating the export of a dog would be well advised to contact the headquarters of the State Veterinary Service, in plenty of time, at Hook Rise South, Tolworth, Surbiton, Surrey – Telephone

01–337–6611, asking for the department dealing with the export of dogs and cats. (See also Travelling with dogs)

Insurance – third party and veterinary fees

The cost of veterinary medicine and surgery is high. The high standards we quite rightly demand for our dogs cannot be achieved and maintained if the economics of practice are not carefully monitored. Drugs are very expensive, a fact from which our National Health Service shields us.

While the cost of veterinary treatment in this country is unlikely to put anybody in the bankruptcy court, a serious road accident or prolonged period of disease can produce an unpleasant dent in the family budget.

Civil action for damages in the courts if your dog is responsible for injury to others, either as a consequence of a road accident or because it attacked somebody, may well be another financial story.

To guard against these eventualities there are several companies specialising in canine insurance. It would seem prudent for owners to consider insurance for their dog.

Part Three

Disease

An animal may be said to have or be diseased if it fails to behave, or its body fails to function, normally. The art and science of diagnosis practised by the veterinary surgeon depends on the ability to take a detailed history, make a careful clinical examination, and to utilise laboratory aids and other ancillary services, e.g. X-ray. Only on the basis of the information gleaned against an extensive knowledge of the normal functions of the body will a diagnosis be possible.

The owner, however, for whom this book is intended, will often be aware of only one or two more obvious symptoms, and it will be as a consequence of these symptoms that they will feel the concern which stimulates a visit to their veterinary surgeon. With this in mind a list of symptoms is provided first, together with some of the diseases they may suggest. This is followed by a detailed consideration of the more commonly encountered diseases of the dog.

This section could not, and does not attempt to, replace your veterinary surgeon. Its task is simply to inform. Hopefully it will recapitulate and possibly expand general aspects of the discussion which takes place in the consulting room. It is not a guide to home doctoring.

Veterinary surgeons

The relationship between a dog owner and a veterinary surgeon is close and frequently charged with emotion born of concern, compassion and sometimes despair. If it is to prove satisfactory then it must be based on understanding, respect and above all mutual trust.

In rural areas the choice of a veterinary surgeon is often limited by distance, one is forced to use whichever is locally available. In towns there is often a choice not only of veterinary surgeon but of type of practice. There is not an easy way of selecting the veterinary surgeon which will suit your needs. Local gossip may be bigoted and ill informed. The only method is to suck it and see. Some veterinary surgeons work alone in single-handed practices. Many clients prefer the personal service offered by this system and providing you like the

The author and Fred, star of the television series 'The Duchess of Duke Street'. Fred is owned by Mrs Geddes.

veterinary surgeon concerned it can be a rewarding and profitable relationship. Many practices involve several veterinary surgeons. This is certainly of benefit to the veterinary surgeons concerned who have more free time for pleasure, professional reading and even research, but there is the disadvantage of lack of continuity which is only partially solved by a case card. In recent years single-handed practitioners in urban areas have co-operated with other professional colleagues in the area to achieve a measure of free time. This compromise seems in many cases to provide the best of both worlds. Whatever system is chosen owners have the right to expect a total commitment to the welfare of dogs accepted as patients by the veterinary surgeon. The law demands and the owner can anticipate that a veterinary surgeon use all the skill and knowledge at his or her disposal to treat a patient. Equally the veterinary surgeon has the right to receive honourable and responsible behaviour in return. It is frustrating, not to say infuriating, to spend a good deal of time and thought on a clinical case only to hear that for some inexplicable reason the owner has without consultation dispensed with one's services and taken their dog to another veterinary surgeon for treatment. Such action is not only unethical it is positively stupid. The veterinary profession has a very strict ethical code of practice. This has been devised and is imposed upon members of the profession in the interests of the animal patients. When one veterinary surgeon has been dealing with a case it is an offence against the ethical code of the profession for another veterinary surgeon to take the case over without both the knowledge and consent of the first veterinary surgeon. This prevents the loss of valuable time and unnecessary distress to the patient while the second veterinary surgeon retraces the diagnostic and therapeutic procedures of the first.

Second opinions

There may come a time when a protracted case engenders concern either in the veterinary surgeon or in the client. In such a case it is not only reasonable but sensible for a second opinion to be sought. If the veterinary surgeon is unhappy about the case he will suggest a second opinion and will invariably indicate a colleague whom he feels would be competent to make pertinent observations. If owners are unhappy about the progress of a case they are within their rights to indicate their disquiet and if they so desire ask for a second opinion. Most veterinary surgeons will co-operate with such a request and will again usually suggest a suitable colleague. If the client's veterinary surgeon is quite happy about the case he may choose simply to ask a local colleague to examine the animal to confirm his diagnosis and treatment. This usually reassures the owner. If however he feels the case to be particularly difficult or of an obscure origin he will often suggest a specialist in the particular part of the body or type of disease. Such specialists are usually found in university departments.

Veterinary hospitals

In recent years the Royal College of Veterinary Surgeons – the governing body of the veterinary profession – has allowed the term 'hospital' to be used to describe some veterinary establishments which conform to certain physical standards. I believe this decision was ill considered. The term hospital in everyday use means an establishment where specialised attention can be sought from clinicians (veterinary or medical) who have made an academic study of a discrete branch of medicine or surgery. The so called 'veterinary hospitals' are surely the premises of private veterinary surgeons, and most certainly do not offer the specialised attention that the word 'hospital' implies. The service a member of the public will receive in these establishments is usually well up to the average standard expected of a practising veterinary surgeon. It is most certainly not superior and clients who choose a 'veterinary hospital' should not be deceived into believing that their animal is receiving the attentions of a specialist consultant.

Modern drugs

There is a tendency among certain sections of the public to be sceptical of, or reject, the use of modern drugs, in particular the administration of antibiotics. While it is true that diligence and moderation must always be the watchword, the real value of modern medicine must not be denied. It has been suggested by cynics, with some foundation of truth, that before the discovery of general application of penicillin the medical and veterinary profession killed as many as it cured. It is certainly true that modern drugs have improved health, and enabled conditions previously fatal, to be successfully treated.

The current fashion for alternative and fringe medicine is a reaction against unfortunate episodes like the Thalidomide tragedy. While these methods should be investigated and the most beneficial aspects of them incorporated in orthodox medical practice, there is no doubt that a return to superstition and witchcraft, using methods for which there is no scientific basis, would be a retrograde step.

Handling dogs in surgery

Veterinary surgeons prefer, indeed many expect, owners to handle their own dogs. Always, but always, take your dog to the surgery on a lead. Even the best behaved dog may prove difficult in these surroundings. There may also be nervous cats in the waiting room and you will not be popular if your dog frightens them because it will make them difficult to handle for examination.

When you get into the consulting room KEEP YOUR DOG ON THE LEAD. It is amazing how many owners remove this most effective control measure, just when it is most needed. Perhaps it reminds them of undressing for the doctor. You may be asked to put the dog on the table. If not ask if you should. All but the largest dogs are best examined on the consulting table.

To lift a large dog place one arm around the front of his chest and the other either under its belly or around the hind legs just above the hock. Small dogs can be grasped with two hands around the chest or with one hand under the chest, the abdomen being supported by the arm. Once on the table DO NOT TAKE THE LEAD OFF. Keep hold of the dog making sure it doesn't move while the veterinary surgeon examines it. If it is necessary to put a tape on the dog because it is inclined to snap or bite hold the dog securely behind the ears while it is applied. (See Nursing)

Home visits

Home visits present a number of problems. They are very time consuming and therefore expensive. Veterinary surgeons prefer to be employed treating animals not being taxi drivers. If at all possible take your dog to the surgery. You are not justified in asking for a home visit because you have a difficult dog. All too often difficult dogs are easier to handle in the surgery, where the veterinary surgeon has skilled assistants to help control the dog. Very sick dogs often need treatment which can only be given in the surgery. It is pointless to claim that the dog cannot be moved. If it needs specialised treatment or a surgical operation, it will have to be taken to the surgery. A few types of cases are better seen at home. Some post operative cases should be visited as should some dogs with severe heart disease.

If you do ask for a home visit make sure you can handle the dog for examination. Have sufficient help at hand. I recall going miles on a very busy day at the request of an owner only to be told with delight when I arrived that I would never get near the dog. He was quite correct. It was a half savage dobermann snarling at me from behind a cupboard. The owner was too frightened to go near it. When it was approached it began to emerge and attack.

If it is a small dog, have a table prepared with a clean blanket on top to prevent the dog slipping. Provide washing facilities with a clean towel.

Giving a history

Marshall your thoughts before you are called into the consulting room. The veterinary surgeon wants a clear description of the problem so you must be able to say concisely why you have brought the dog. Veterinary surgeons will then ask a number of questions relating to the dog's behaviour and habits. Remember it is changes which are significant. If asked whether the dog is drinking normally, do not reply that he never drinks much. It is of no interest what he normally does only how normality has altered. Therefore you answer either that he is drinking normally or, for example, that for two days he has been drinking a great deal more than usual. Mention anything that you have noticed which may be of significance but do not be verbose and do not offer your opinion. You have sought a consultation to allow the veterinary surgeon to evaluate the condition and make a diagnosis.

Anatomy
Skeletal system
The boney structure of the body which supports the soft tissue. It is composed of a number of bones which are joined together at the joints. Bones are not solid but composed of a complex cellular structure.

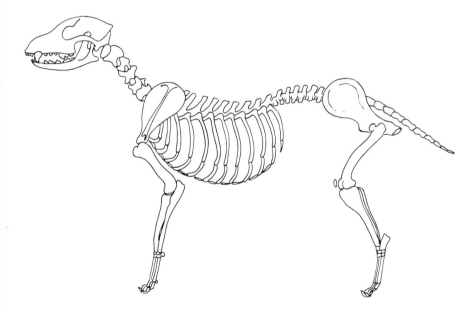

Muscular system
Muscles are attached to the bones. When they contract they move the bones. Muscles make up the bulk of the body form.

Alimentary tract
The purpose of the alimentary tract is to break down the food which enters the mouth into small particles. These can be absorbed into the blood system and transported around the body where they can be used to provide energy.

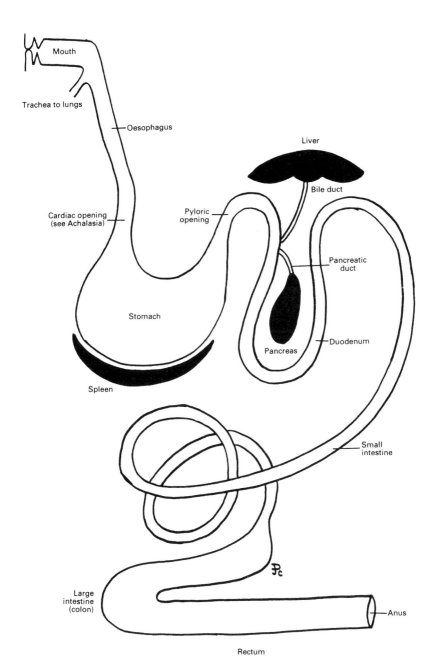

Gastro intestinal tract

Respiratory system

The body needs oxygen to enable the food particles to be used – a kind of controlled burning – to provide energy. The respiratory system draws fresh air, containing oxygen, into the lungs where it passes into the blood system and in which it is transported around the body to the sites where it is required.

The waste product of burning, carbon dioxide, is brought to the lungs by the blood stream and then breathed out.

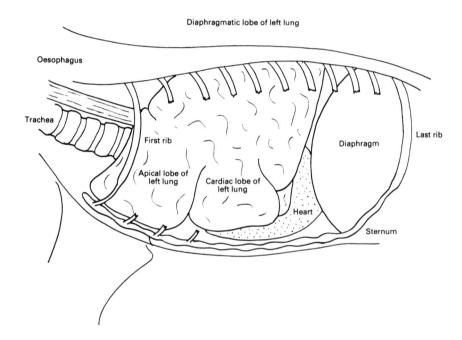

Left ribs removed to show position of respiratory organs in chest

Urogenital system

This is really two closely related systems. The urinary system which removes waste products at the kidneys and passes them out via the bladder in the urine and the genital system which is concerned with reproduction.

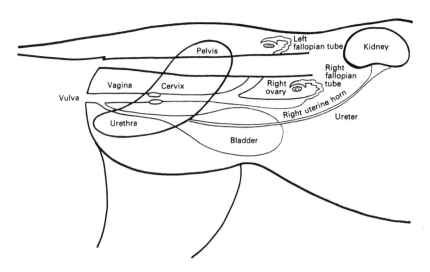

Female urogenital system

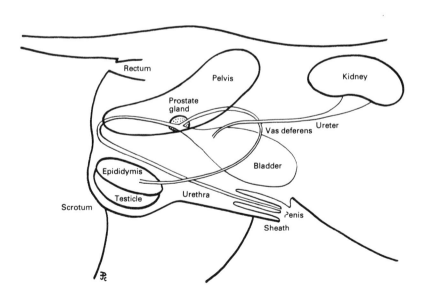

Male urogenital system

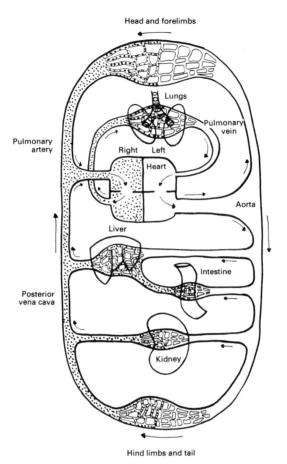

Head and forelimbs

Lungs

Pulmonary vein

Pulmonary artery

Right   Left

Heart

Aorta

Liver

Intestine

Posterior vena cava

Kidney

Hind limbs and tail

Circulation of the blood

Circulatory system

The transport system of the body. Blood is pumped around the body by the heart. The blood carries food from the alimentary tract, oxygen from the lungs, waste products to the kidneys and carbon dioxide to the lungs.

The heart is divided into four chambers. Blood returns from the body to the right auricle. It then passes to the right ventricle from where it is pumped to the lungs. Returning to the heart from the lungs it enters the left auricle. Passing to the left ventricle it is pumped again around the body. Blood going to the lungs from the right ventricle is low in oxygen and high in carbon dioxide. After passing through the lungs it has gained oxygen and lost its carbon dioxide.

Nervous system

Consists of the brain, the spinal cord, and the nerves. The nervous system controls the body. The brain receives information from all parts of the body all the time and is constantly transmitting information to tell the body what to do.

Sensory system

Includes the five senses – sight, hearing, smell, touch and taste – which relay information to the brain telling it about the environment and any changes which are occurring.

Symptoms affecting the head

Cold nose

This classic symptom handed down to us by generations of old wives is thought by many dog owners to be a definitive guide to a dog's health. Sadly this belief is without foundation in truth.

A dog may have a dry nose if it has a temperature but a snooze in front of a fire can produce the same effect. Equally animals with severe functional disorders like heart, kidney and liver may well have a cold wet nose. No reliance then on this symptom.

Eyes

Any problem associated with eyes should be regarded as serious. Professional advice should be sought without delay. (See Eye disease)
1 Rubbing eyes may indicate conjunctivitis, corneal ulcers, or glaucoma. In puppies and young adults it may in addition suggest inherited or congenital conditions like entropion, ectropion, distichiasis and trichiasis. (See Eye disease and Eyelid disease)
2 Discharge from eyes may indicate infected conjunctivitis or the presence of secondary bacterial invasion following more serious conditions. (See Eye disease, Distemper, Canine viral hepatitis, Leptospirosis, Pyometritis)
3 Red eyes, bloodshot whites of the eye, is a symptom of conjunctivitis but it can also indicate a general infection of some kind including distemper. It is often present in an infection of the womb, seen in unspayed bitches, after the age of seven, called pyometritis. (See Eye disease, Distemper, Canine viral hepatitis, Leptospirosis, Pyometritis)
4 Blinking eyes (photophobia), common in many eye conditions particularly corneal ulcers.
5 'Skin across the eye'. This is the third eyelid, technically the nictitating membrane, which covers the eye to give added protection when the eye is closed. Dogs half asleep sometimes show this but if it is

apparent when the dog is awake it may indicate conjunctivitis, general infection or corneal ulcers.

6 Nictitating membrane enlarged. (See 5 above) Occasionally a gland (Harder's gland) on the third eyelid becomes enlarged. (See Eyelid disease)

7 Swollen eye – due to an increase in internal pressure, glaucoma or a swelling – abscess or growth – behind the eye. This is always very serious and attention should be sought at once.

8 Blue eye – Eyes look blue for two reasons: The cornea (See diagram of Eye Anatomy page 138) may be damaged due to local infection, trauma (a foreign body like a thorn damaging the eye) or more rarely due to general infection (canine viral hepatitis). Alternatively the lens may become opaque (cataract). (See Eye disease, Blue eye)

9 Wall eye – This is due to lack of pigment or colour in the iris. (See diagram Eye Anatomy) It may affect part or all of the iris of one eye or both eyes. It is common in border collies. It is not a disease. Its appearance, being unusual, causes some people consternation and much nonsense is talked about its relationship to bad temperament.

10 Blindness – various causes – seek attention.

Shaking head

By far the commonest reason for a dog shaking its head is ear disease. These cases should always be examined by a veterinary surgeon and should never be treated with proprietary drugs. Ear conditions are rarely killing diseases but untreated they cause severe discomfort, often with considerable pain to the dog.

Hanging head to one side

If very sudden in onset, particularly after a summer walk, it is possibly a grass seed (wild barley awn) in the ear. Extremely uncomfortable, needs urgent attention. (See Ear disease, Haematoma)

Scratching ear

Due to irritation in the ear or parasites on the ear flaps. (See Ear disease, Skin disease)

Swelling of ear flap

This is often due to a haematoma (blood blister) of the ear flap. It will need treatment itself but more important is to treat the head shaking or scratching which caused it. (See Ear disease, Haematoma)

Pawing at mouth

This is usually very sudden in onset. It is often accompanied by salivation. The dog can become quite frantic. Commonly due to a bone lodged in teeth. Less frantic pawing may be due to wasp or bee stings. Occasionally due to a bad tooth. (See Glossitis, Teeth)

Salivation (drooling)

Commonly seen in loose lipped dogs like spaniels, setters, St Bernards, and bloodhounds, as a normal occurrence. Many dogs salivate at the thought of food. Also seen while begging from their owner. Severe salivation unconnected with eating often accompanies a foreign body like a bone in the mouth or in the oesophagus. (See Glossitis, Pharyngitis, Rabies, Tonsillitis)

Smell from mouth (Halitosis)

Sensitive owners often seek advice about bad breath, and when examined the only smell apparent is normal dog breath – a little meaty perhaps. After a lifetime among animals veterinary surgeons become if not immune, certainly less sensitive.

Genuine complaints about bad breath may be due to tartar coated teeth or gum infection (gingivitis). Severe cases progress to paradontal disease. It may also be due to stomatitis, tonsillitis, pharyngitis or laryngitis. Infected labial folds, more common in loose lipped breeds like the spaniel, produce the most incredible smell for such a small problem. Fortunately the latter condition responds well to surgery. (See Labial folds, Teeth)

Bad teeth

Dogs rarely suffer from dental caries (holes in the teeth) like humans. In most cases 'bad teeth' presented by owners are caused by an accumulation of tartar on the teeth – substance very like fur in kettles. As this builds up on the teeth, food particles, trapped between the tartar and the gums, go bad and infection results. The infection causes the gum to retreat from the root which in turn leads to loose teeth. A patient so afflicted is described as suffering from parodontal disease.

Pitted teeth

Some adult teeth erupt with poor enamel. They appear pitted and brown. These are called distemper teeth. (See Teeth)

Choking or gagging

Some dogs have bouts when they seem to almost choke or gag. These are spasmodic often, but not always, occurring when they are excited like going for a walk. This is due to the soft palate flipping into the larynx and obstructing the air flow, or it may be due to a temporary nervous constriction of the vocal cords. It is not serious. You and the dog have to live with it.

Discharge from nose

This should always be considered serious. It can be a symptom of general infection like distemper. It may be due to infection of the sinuses (sinusitis). Occasionally foreign bodies (grass awns or wild barley being the most common) gain entry to the nose to cause time consuming problems and discomfort. It may also be due to cancer within the sinuses. (See Canine viral hepatitis, Distemper, Pneumonia, Rhinitis, Sinusitis)

Most nasal discharge becomes rapidly purulent (pus). A blow on the head or nose may produce blood. (See Epistaxis) It is useful when consulting the veterinary surgeon to be able to observe if the discharge comes from both nostrils or from only one.

Deafness

Young dogs are occasionally deaf. While dogs are sometimes deaf due to an inherited factor, old dogs may develop deafness for which there is at present no cure. Subtle and sophisticated tests for deafness are not available to veterinary surgeons since dogs will not indicate when they hear small noises. We must rely on the response to a clapped hand or a called pet name. Beware of the older dog who develops convenience deafness, i.e. the one that only hears when it suits its purpose.

Symptoms affecting the gastro intestinal tract

Not eating (Anorexia)

Most dogs are keen to eat anything put before them, but few dogs, particularly the smaller toy breeds, are finicky eaters and may quite regularly refuse food for a day now and again. The sudden refusal of food however by dogs which are normally dedicated gluttons should always be regarded as a serious symptom until otherwise proved and veterinary advice should be sought without delay. (See Canine viral hepatitis, Distemper, Enteritis, Foreign bodies in the alimentary canal, Gastritis, Hepatitis, Leptospirosis, Metritis, Nephritis, Pancreatitis, Pyometritis, Tonsillitis, Tuberculosis)

Drinking

Dogs generally drink once or twice each day. They commonly drink after exercise. Water should be available at all times. A sudden increase in the consumption of water is a very important symptom indeed, indicating a number of serious conditions. In dogs of all ages it may suggest stomach disorder (gastritis), poisoning, inflammation of the bladder (cystitis), various diseases of the liver and kidneys (hepatitis and nephritis), and both forms of diabetes (diabetes insipidus and diabetes mellitus). In middle-aged or old dogs excessive thirst indicates degenerative liver and kidney conditions, while bitches from early middle age which drink more than usual may have womb problems (metritis or pyometritis). It should be emphasised that excessive thirst rarely occurs on its own and it is the combination of symptoms which identify the diagnosis. It is often useful to the veterinary surgeon if a urine sample is brought to the consultation. This should be collected in a clean flat dish or saucer and transported in a clean well rinsed bottle. Reduced water intake is extremely rare. (See Canine viral hepatitis, Cystitis, Diabetes mellitus, Gastritis, Hepatitis, Leptospirosis, Metritis, Nephritis, Pyometritis, Urolithiasis)

Vomiting

Dogs vomit very readily, more readily than do human beings. We have seen that all adult members of a dog or wolf pack will regurgitate food for puppies quite normally. (See Behaviour of wild dogs and wolves) A few bitches will vomit spasmodically during the period of false pregnancy. This is probably related to normal weaning behaviour and, providing there are no other symptoms, need be of no concern.

Some dogs will vomit occasionally without other symptoms or any apparent reason. This may occur after the dog has eaten grass. (See Eating grass) It may be the dog's method of rejecting the rubbish so many dogs consume with such enthusiasm.

Apart from these few exceptions persistent vomiting, i.e. several times within a few hours, must be considered serious and professional assistance sought without delay. Vomiting accompanies a great number of conditions. It is useful to observe and then to tell the veterinary surgeon if the vomit contains food, is frothy, or has a yellow or bloodstained appearance. So called projectile vomiting where fluid stomach contents are produced as a fountain-like arc is associated with the specific conditions of puppies and young dogs, achalasia and pyloric stenosis. (See Achalasia, Canine viral hepatitis, Concussion, Diabetes mellitus, Distemper, Foreign bodies in the alimentary canal, Gastritis, Hepatitis, Leptospirosis, Nephritis, Parvovirus, Poisoning. Prostatitis, Peritonitis, Pyloric stenosis and also Pyometritis, Tuberculosis, Intussusception)

Constipation

Constipation is evidenced to the owner by persistent straining to pass faeces without the desired result. It may be due to foreign objects in the gut – bones, bits of rubber, wood etc. (See Rectal obstruction), poor gut action more common in old dogs, prostate problems in older males (See Prostatic hyperplasia), or cancer of the bowel. It can be confused with anal sac impaction or infection and MUST BE DISTINGUISHED FROM DIARRHOEA. Long-coated dogs may get the hair around the anus matted with diarrhoea. This mat may effectively block the anus and prevent the passage of watery faeces. It is not unusual for owners to see a dog in such a plight, assume it is constipated and administer appropriate medicaments with sometimes very serious results. Simple constipation is rare in the dog. (See Anal sacs and anal glands, Foreign bodies in the alimentary canal, Prostatic hyperplasia, Rectal obstruction, Rickets)

Diarrhoea

Diarrhoea is a symptom not a disease. It has very many causes, which range from eating rubbish or bad food to cancer of the bowel. It should always be treated seriously. As a first aid measure stop feeding the dog and administer kaolin. If the symptoms do not abate within a very few hours, seek professional help. Diarrhoea containing blood (dysentery) may be extremely serious. Veterinary advice should be sought as a matter of extreme urgency. (See Canine viral hepatitis, Coccidiosis, Distemper, Enteritis, Hepatitis, Leptospirosis, Pancreatitis, Parvovirus, Poisoning, Rickets, Tuberculosis)

Grumbling, rumbling or noisy abdomen

Some dogs have occasional bouts of noise emanating from the depths of their bowels. It may or may not be accompanied by the passage of foul smelling gas from the anus. Dogs which suffer these cacophonies may not themselves appear ill and are then no more than a social embarrassment. Others are quite clearly unwell for several hours while the attack lasts. These dogs should all be examined carefully by a veterinary surgeon to make sure there is no serious cause for the problem. Very often however the condition is due to a mild spasmodic dysfunction of the intestinal tract and owners can then be provided with a simple medicine for use when an attack occurs. (See Flatulence)

Flatulence

The passage of foul smelling gases through the anus. This is a natural process. Gases build up in the intestines as a result of the digestive process. Some dogs, notably the bull breeds, seem to be more productive than others. When the levels are socially unacceptable, adjustment of diet and mild medication may alleviate or reduce the problem. It cannot be solved completely.

Eating grass

All dogs will eat occasional mouthfuls of grass given the opportunity. They seem to prefer those with the coarser blades. The reason for this is not clearly understood but is probably a method of adding bulk or fibre to the diet, now recognised as an important factor in good digestion. Grass certainly can not be utilised as a food by flesh eating animals. In addition to this normal intake of grass, dogs will sometimes eat large quantities of grass and promptly vomit. In this case the dog may eat grass as a normal response to digestive unease or directly to make itself sick, but the latter seems unlikely since dogs vomit so easily.

Incontinence (faecal)

The uncontrolled passage of faeces may be due to damage to nervous tissue either in the spine, commonly caused by intervertebral disc protrusion or a broken back. Nervous tissue may be damaged locally near the anus. Occasionally the muscles controlling the anus are themselves damaged which produces the same effect. Senile dogs are sometimes incontinent.

Symptoms affecting the respiratory system

Discharge from the nose, a symptom of upper respiratory infection has been dealt with under 'Symptoms affecting the head'.

Hiccuping

This occurs frequently in puppies as it does in children. It usually follows feeding. It is of no consequence. Adult dogs rarely if ever hiccup.

Coughing

May be an indication of several different conditions affecting the respiratory system, or it may suggest heart disease. Laryngitis, bronchitis, pneumonia and pleurisy produce coughing as do several well known infectious diseases – distemper and kennel cough. Dogs with heart disease, notably mitral valve incompetence will also cough. Coughing is invariably a serious symptom and should be treated professionally. (See Bronchitis, Distemper, Heart disease, Kennel cough, Laryngitis, Pharyngitis, Pleurisy, Pneumonia, Tonsillitis, and Tuberculosis)

Sneezing

Usually a symptom of upper respiratory infection including infected sinuses (sinusitis). A sudden onset of severe sneezing may be due to a foreign body, e.g. a wild barley seed in the nose, or inhalation of an irritant substance. A very rare parasite which lives in the nose can cause persistent sneezing. Cancer of the sinus is not uncommon in older dogs. (See Epistaxis, Rhinitis, Sinusitis)

Bad breathing (Dysponea)

May be due to respiratory infection. e.g. pneumonia, pleurisy. Can result from cancer of the lung or heart disease. Always considered a serious symptom. (See Ascites, Bronchitis, Diaphragmatic hernia,

Distemper, Epistoxis, Gastric distension, Heart disease, Heart stroke, Pleurisy, Pneumonia, Tuberculosis)

Symptoms affecting the urogenital system – male
Swollen protruding penis
Owners sometimes find their dog with an enlarged penis and the dog apparently distressed. This is usually due to an erection. It will regress normally. Occasionally a tight foreskin seems to prevent retraction. Easing the sheath over the penis is usually successful. A lubricating jelly may help.

Discharge from penis
This is usually due to an infection within the sheath. (See Balanitis)

Blood from penis
May be due to a bite on the penis. A not uncommon problem in free roaming dogs. It can indicate severe bladder problems (cystitis), stones in the bladder (urolithiasis) or disease of the prostate gland (prostatitis).

Swollen testicles
Testicles may appear swollen for two main reasons. They are either infected (orchitis) often as a result of being bitten during a fight or because of segeral types of cancer. (See Testicular tumours)

Undescending testicles
One or both testicles may fail to descend from the abdomen to the scrotum. It is essential for sperm production, but not male hormone production, that the testicles be in the scrotum. A dog will therefore act as a male, will mate, but will not father puppies. If one testicle only is descended then the dog can father pups from the one normal testicle. Dogs with one or two undescended testicles, monorchid or cryptorchid are not eligible for showing and should not be used for breeding as the condition is inherited. Sertoli cell tumours are more common in undescended testicles. (See Testicular tumours)

Symptoms affecting the urogenital system – female
Licking vulva
Bitches on heat lick their vulva frequently as do bitches about to whelp and during whelping. Such bitches usually lick their vulva on returning from a walk and after urination. Persistent licking without being on heat is abnormal. It may indicate vaginitis, problems with skin around the vulva, vulvitis, cystitis, or pyometritis.

Blood from vulva
Blood is normally expelled from the vulva for the first two weeks of the

heat. (See Canine sexuality) Blood or bloody discharge extending beyond the end of the three weeks period of heat is not normal. It suggests pyometritis. Blood from the vulva may suggest cystitis, a wound to the vagina during mating, stones in the bladder (urolithiasis) or cancer.

Discharge from vulva

A yellow discharge from the vulva occurs occasionally in young bitches due to a vaginitis. Unspayed bitches, usually over seven years of age, which show a purulent discharge up to two months after heat may have pyometritis.

General symptoms of the urogenital system

Urination

Frequent passage of small drops of urine is normal in the male dog. Dominant bitches in a pack and bitches on heat will also mark frequently when out walking. Owners should note sudden changes in the pattern of urination. In both sexes persistent straining without result is a serious symptom indicating cystitis, stones in bladder, (urolithiasis) or more rarely cancer and prostatic hyperplasia in the male.

Incontinence (urinary)

The uncontrolled passing of urine is usually due to damage to the nervous control of the opening of the bladder. This may be due to intervertebral disc protrusion or physical trauma resulting from a car accident. Urinary incontinence in old spayed bitches occurs quite frequently and can often be alleviated with hormone treatment. (See Canine sexuality)

Obtaining a urine sample

A urine sample is often requested by the veterinary surgeon. To obtain some take the dog out on a lead first thing in the morning, when he or she is a little desperate. Take with you a clean flat dish or saucer. As the dog performs place the saucer to catch a sample. A small amount is sufficient for most purposes. Transfer the sample to a clean bottle (sterile plastic pots are often provided). Label with your name, the dog's name and the date and time of collection and take to the veterinary surgeon as soon as possible for analysis.

Symptoms of the central nervous system

Twitching (Chorea)

Twitching of groups of muscles particularly when resting is a common sequela to distemper.

Fits

Dogs which suddenly fall or collapse may be limp or go rigid. Fits usually last only a few seconds or continue for a minute or so. When the dog recovers it may appear dazed or anxious. During the fit it may gnash its teeth and froth at the mouth. Do not touch a dog in a fit. Simply make sure it cannot hurt itself. Leave it alone until it recovers. Fits may be caused by heart disease or by some disorder of the brain, stroke, meningitis, or encephalitis. Not infrequently dogs suffer from epilepsy. Diagnosis can be confirmed by taking ECG (Electrocardiogram) and/or EEG (Electroencephalogram).

Temperament

Veterinary surgeons are frequently consulted because dogs have unsuitable temperaments or undesirable behaviour traits. These problems are often extremely difficult to diagnose and even more difficult to solve. In some cases the problem may arise as a result of organic disease. (See Concussion, Distemper, Encephalitis, Hydrocephalitis, Meningitis, Neuritis, Rabies) It may be due to inherited mental instability. Sometimes cyclic changes are to blame, the most common being false pregnancy in the bitch. (See Canine sexuality) Bitches with false pregnancies are likely to be bad tempered and more aggressive than usual. Normal behavioural development in male dogs in reaching maturity attempt to improve their position in the dominance hierarchy, is sometimes the cause. (See Part I, Behaviour of domestic dogs) All too often temperamental problems are due to inexperienced owners who fail to train and discipline their dogs. The dogs take advantage of inept handling, becoming dominant and are presented to the veterinary surgeon with unsuitable behaviour well established. The problem in this case is twofold. First the dog's behaviour needs correcting which is by no means easy or even possible. Secondly the owner's attitude to dogs needs adjusting to prevent the problem recurring. The old saying 'prevention is better than cure' is never truer than in this situation. If you are an inexperienced owner or you lack confidence seek help from one of the excellent training classes (the term dog training is a misnomer, they are really owner training classes, the dogs go along to help) now available while the dog is still young. (See Part I, Behavioural problems)

Circling

Walking in circles is an indication of brain damage. This is often due to a stroke (clot in the blood circulation in the brain) if sudden in onset. It may also be due to an abscess or cancer in the brain.

Diagnosis and treatment of the cause of lameness needs veterinary attention

Symptoms affecting the locomotor system

Lameness

There are indeed numerous reasons for lameness, from a thorn in the foot through degenerative disease, including arthritis, to malignant cancer of the bone. Differentiation of the cause of lameness requires not only professional experience but often the use of X-rays. (See Arthritis, Cruciate ligament rupture, Dislocation. Fractures, Hip dysplasia, Myositis, Radial paralysis, Slipped disc, Spondylitis)

Weak hind quarters

Several conditions may cause this worrying symptom. It may be due to degeneration of nerves, hip dysplasia, intervertebral disc protrusion, pyometritis, or foreign body obstruction of the colon and rectum. (See Hip dysplasia, Spondylitis)

Dragging hind legs

Dogs drag their hind legs stretched out behind them (compare position adopted for anal gland problems) when there is damage to the spinal cord caused through a broken back or a slipped disc.

Swelling between toes

This may be due either to interdigital cysts or a foreign body, commonly a grass seed, which has worked under the skin. (See Skin disease)

Swollen or sore feet and toes

May be due to interdigital dermatitis or paronychia. (See Skin disease)

Miscellaneous symptoms
Dragging anus along ground – 'skating'
Dogs may be seen to sit with hind legs outstretched forward, tail pointing backwards, dragging themselves along the ground with their forelegs. This is almost invariably due to impaction or infection of the anal sacs, commonly referred to as the anal glands.

Dehydration
Strictly interpreted, dehydration is a reduction in the body fluids, and a blood test is required to ascertain its presence. (See Nephritis, Parvovirus, Poisoning, Pyometritis) Clinically however when dehydration is moderate to severe it can be demonstrated by lifting a handful of skin, most veterinary surgeons lift the skin of the scruff. If upon release, the skin falls straight back into place the dog may be regarded as normal. Conversely if the skin is slow to return to its normal position a degree of dehydration is present. (See Canine viral hepatitis, Diabetes insipidus, Diabetes mellitus, Distemper, Dysentery, Enteritis, Foreign bodies in the alimentary canal, Gastritis, Hepatitis, Leptospirosis)

Jaundice
The eyes, mouth, inside ears and skin may appear yellow. (See Hepatitis, Jaundice)

Lethargy
Lethargy or listlessness is a symptom of many diseases. Indeed it is such a common feature of ill dogs that it is often the first indication that something is wrong.

Losing weight
The reason any animal eats food, its fuel, is to provide energy necessary for its daily activities. If it eats too much food, the surplus is stored as fat for leaner times and it becomes obese. If it eats too little it turns to its store of body fat, begins to use it and loses weight. It is very rare in our over indulgent western society to find owners giving too little food but it does happen. If your dog does appear thin, ask your veterinary surgeon for an opinion, rather than rely on the bar room 'expert', then simply increasing the food may improve matters.

A sudden loss of weight may indicate a number of serious diseases. (See Achalasia, Cancer, Diabetes, Hepatitis, Leptospirosis, Nephritis, Pancreatitis, Poisoning, Pyloric, Stenosis, Rickets, Tuberculosis, Roundworms, Tapeworms)

Obesity
Obesity is almost always a disease or condition imposed upon pet dogs by over indulgent owners of the affluent society. (See Part II, Obesity)

Skin disease

Skin disease is manifest by a number of symptoms. The causes of skin disease are legion and complicated. Any suspicion of a skin problem should be presented for diagnosis promptly. Neglected skin diseases are more difficult to clear. Symptoms of skin disease include scratching and biting (pruritus), dry coarse coat, loss of hair, broken hair, red skin, wet skin (often in patches), scurf or dandruff, obvious parasites (fleas and lice) and spots filled with clear fluid (vesicles) or pus (pustules). (See Skin disease)

Sudden pain

Dogs are quite often presented at the surgery for crying out or screaming when touched. This symptom, usually sudden in onset, is naturally, extremely worrying to the owners. In addition the dogs may appear reluctant to move and appear dejected. No other symptoms to help localise the pain may be present. The causes of severe pain are of course legion and since veterinary surgeons are unable to communicate verbally with their patients this particular symptom can present real problems of diagnosis. The cause may be due to some form of accident – a kick or car accident. It can be due to awkward movements which cause sprained tendons or pulled muscles. Quite commonly it is due to 'back problems'. Pain in the back may be muscular or more commonly results from protrusion of an intervertebral disc (slipped disc) or spondylitis. It is of course quite impossible to list all causes of sudden pain. Professional advice must be enlisted. (See Cancer, Canine viral hepatitis, Intussusception, Leptospirosis, Mastitis, Meningitis, Nephritis, Peritonitis, Prostatitis, Slipped disc)

Swellings on body

The sudden appearance of lumps or swellings quite naturally causes concern. They are not always easy to differentiate and should always be examined professionally as it is often prudent to resort rapidly to surgery if a cure is to be assured.

Hernias and ruptures are not uncommon. Young animals commonly have umbilical hernias in the middle of the abdomen. Old male dogs occasionally develop a perineal rupture (often wrongly called perineal hernia) to one side of and below the tail while dogs of all ages and sexes can have an inguinal hernia – a swelling in the groin.

Haematomas are blood blisters. They can occur anywhere and are due to some form of damage which causes a blood vessel to burst allowing free blood to collect under the skin. A common site for a haematoma is on the ear flap which swells sometimes to enormous proportions.

Abscesses are swellings produced by the local accumulation of pus. They are often, but not always, hot, red and painful. Slow forming abscesses may develop a thick wall in which case they may not be hot or painful.

Cysts are fluid cavities. They are rarely painful and are soft to touch. Cysts are usually removed surgically without problem.

Cancerous growths or tumours may be benign which means they do not reform when removed and do not spread to other parts of the body. Malignant tumours, the type of cancer most people understandably dread, will often regrow at the original site if removed surgically, and more worrying still spread to other vital parts of the body like the lungs, liver and spleen. (See Cancer, Haematoma, Hernias, Mammary tumours, Orchitis, Testicular tumours)

Swollen abdomen

Abdomens swell normally during pregnancy and to a lesser degree during false pregnancy. They may also enlarge with roundworms in puppies, womb infection (pyometritis), cancer, and dropsy (ascites). If the swelling is in a large dog, is sudden in onset and appears to be causing considerable distress it may be a case of gastric torsion or gastric distension. Professional help in the latter case is essential immediately if the dog's life is to be saved. (See also Roundworms)

Swollen breasts (Mammary glands)

A bitch's breasts swell during pregnancy as they prepare to produce milk and remain swollen while she is feeding the pups (lactation). When the pups are fully weaned the breasts usually return to normal. In some cases they do remain a little pendulous. Bitches with a false pregnancy may well have swollen breasts and even produce milk. This normally resolves itself without treatment.

If the breasts become swollen, hot, red and painful to the touch they may have mastitis. (See Part II, Breeding) Mastitis usually occurs during lactation but can occur at any time. Swelling or hard lumps in breasts may also be due to mammary tumours. Mammary tumours tend to grow over several months, or years, often increasing rapidly in size during false pregnancy.

Temperature

The normal temperature of the dog is 101.5 °F. The temperature can be slightly raised by anxiety or pain. It will be raised considerably if a dog has been recently exercised. In most cases however a temperature of 102.5 °F is significant of some kind of infection. In severe infection temperatures may be up to 106 °F. Low temperatures are seen in functional diseases of the body, like heart disease, nephritis, and also in gastro-enteritis. The body temperature of a bitch quite normally drops a few hours before she gives birth, although this is not invariable and is therefore an unreliable guide. The body temperature usually drops before death although this may not occur where death is caused by severe infection.

Taking a dog's temperature

You need an assistant to hold the dog's head. Take a normal clinical thermometer and flick it down in the normal way. Dip it in a lubricating substance such as petroleum jelly or liquid paraffin. If you are right handed grasp the dog's tail in your right hand and insert it for two or three inches through the anus into the rectum. Leave in place for a minute, twisting the thermometer slightly to right or left, to bring the bulb into contact with the wall of the rectum, and then withdraw. Wipe the instrument clean on cotton wool and read.

Doggy smell

Owners sometimes complain of a doggy smell! This may be an over sensitivity to normal canine odour. Perhaps more frequent bathing would help. (See Part II, Bathing) Male dogs may have a stronger smell than bitches. There are several conditions which give rise to an offensive smell and for which treatment is possible. (See Anal sacs and anal glands, Ear disease, Flatulence, Labial folds, Teeth)

Reluctance to sit

Suggests a degree of discomfort or pain in some part of the body. Careful clinical examination is usually essential to identify the cause. Several conditions are possible. (See Arthritis, Dislocation, Fractures, Gastric distension and torsion, Hip dysplasia, Peritonitis, Slipped disc, Urolithiasis)

Reluctance to lie down

Another symptom which may suggest pain. In some cases where dogs appear distressed and show breathing difficulties it may be due to some obstruction to respiration rather than pain. (See Arthritis, Ascites, Diaphragmatic hernia, Peritonitis, Pleurisy, Pneumonia, Slipped disc)

Self mutilation

Mild self mutilation sometimes in the form of persistent chewing, particularly of feet, may be due to either a skin disease or as a habit to relieve tension rather like nail biting in humans. Severe mutilation may be due to neuritis.

Moving rice grains round the anus

Small rice grain-like objects which may move are the ripe segments of tapeworm. (See Tapeworms)

A–Z OF DISEASES

Abscess
An abscess is the local accumulation of pus. It is often surrounded by a wall of fibrous tissue, produced by the body, to localise the problem. Abscesses are caused by local irritation or infection. They invariably cause swelling of the affected area, are hot and painful to the touch. Treatment consists of the local application of heat – bathing in warm water – to soften the overlying skin. This causes the abscess to point and burst. (Antibiotics are usually administered.)

Achalasia
A condition of puppies which becomes evident soon after weaning. It is caused by action failure of the muscle which controls the entry to the stomach. The muscle fails to relax and food therefore remains in the tube leading from the mouth to the stomach (oesophagus). Soon after eating, since the food cannot pass to the stomach it is vomited back. Puppies so afflicted vomit soon after food, fail to put on weight, and appear thin and dejected. Treatment may be medical, drugs being used to relax the muscular spasm, or surgical. This condition is serious but prompt professional action is often successful.

Amputation
Fortunately amputation of a limb is rarely necessary. When it is there may be considerable disquiet on the part of the owner, who may question the wisdom of keeping a three legged dog. Not only may the owner have misgivings but pressure from local acquaintances often intimidates owners who then elect euthanasia as a convenient alternative.

In practice all except very heavy dogs accommodate well to the amputation of a limb. Man, who is bipedal, walks on two legs and is far more incapacitated by the amputation of a leg or arm than a dog. Providing the dog is not one of the very large breeds – Great Dane, Irish wolfhound, St Bernard etc. – amputation is far preferable to euthanasia.

Anaemia
The body is said to be anaemic when there is less than the normal level present of haemoglobin – the red pigment which transports oxygen around the body. There are numerous causes of anaemia and the establishment of cause is often a complicated procedure. One of the

most obvious and certainly most common is due to blood loss following an accident or following prolonged and difficult surgical operations. Anaemia can be alleviated with a blood transfusion but this will only be temporary unless the cause is diagnosed and corrected.

Anal sacs and anal glands

The paired anal sacs lie either side of and just below the anus at four and eight o'clock. The sacs are surrounded by the anal glands which produce a grey-brown extremely offensive-smelling liquid. The liquid is stored in the sacs. A small tube or duct leads from each sac to open on the anus. As the dog defaecates the pressure of the stool against the anus and surrounding tissue including the anal sacs causes a little of the anal sac fluid to pass up the tube and to be smeared on the stool as it leaves the body. This extremely pungent and persistent liquid gives a characteristic smell to the faeces which can be interpreted by other dogs. Wolves and wild dogs therefore communicate to some extent through the perfume produced by their anal glands. (See Part I, Behaviour of wild dogs and wolves) Dogs and wolves are probably able to recognise each individual by the smell of its anal fluid. The anal sacs and the associated glands have, therefore, an important function.

Anal sacs have their own disease problems. The sacs may become impacted and fail to empty properly. This causes local irritation to the dog which may drag itself along the ground in a sitting position hind legs stretched out forwards, tail backwards and anal region hard against the ground. This is the dog's method of attempting to solve the problem. The dog may also show symptoms of local skin irritation around the base of the tail or may suddenly get up as if bitten and turn to the tail. If these symptoms are exhibited the glands should be expressed using a milking like action. Veterinary surgeons prefer complete emptying by placing a covered finger into the rectum and freeing the gland by squeezing between forefinger and thumb.

Very occasionally the fluid in the glands is dried to a solid state. In this case it is necessary to place a softening fluid into the gland via the small tube which opens onto the anus.

The anal sacs may become infected and the fluid produced contain yellow pus. It is usual to give antibiotics for this condition. The glands may also be flushed out with a cleansing fluid and filled with antibiotics. Infected glands of this type may form an abscess which is extremely painful and may burst through the skin just below the anus.

When the anal sacs cause persistent problems they can be removed surgically along with the anal glands without any apparent social problems for the dog.

Arthritis

Inflammation of the joint. There are several types of arthritis. It may be due to an infection which localises in the joints. It may occur in a single joint or result from a generalised infection which invades the joint tissue. Affected joints are swollen and painful. In many cases the animal is reluctant to move. Body temperature is usually raised. Treatment depends on careful nursing and the use of antibiotics.

Osteoarthritis is the common form of the disease most frequently seen in older dogs. It may be caused by injury to a joint but frequently seems to be part of the process of ageing. The stifle joint, the hip and the spine are sites usually affected. The classic symptom is lameness or in the case of the spine reluctance to move, go up and down steps or even difficulty in assuming the sitting position. Osteoarthritis is a common complication of hip dysplasia. The cause of the disease has been sought for many years but a complete understanding still eludes us. While a cure is not available, considerable relief can be achieved with drugs and the patient's comfort improved. Symptoms are usually gradual in onset, although in a few cases the symptoms appear suddenly. A definite diagnosis of this disease can be made with X-ray examination. There are many treatments for arthritis all of which offer some relief. Considerable progress was made with the discovery of cortisone as its synthetic derivatives. Their use remains important in the management of afflicted patients. Patients with arthritis should be kept in good condition. Obesity is a predisposing factor in the development and exacerbation of arthritis. Fat dogs must be thinned. Good food, dry soft beds, regular short walks and massage of the afflicted limbs will assist medical treatment.

Rheumatoid arthritis which so commonly afflicts man is thought to be rare in the dog although some authorities believe some cases of obscure lameness may be attributed to this condition.

Ascites (dropsy)

This is an accumulation of free fluid in the abdominal cavity. There are several causes for this condition including degeneration of the liver, kidney disease and tumours, which interfere with the circulation of the blood to the liver. The commonest cause however is a functional failure of the right side of the heart. Initially the dog appears well and is usually brought for veterinary attention because the belly is swollen. In later stages of the condition the pressure of the fluid may cause the dog to breathe badly and it may become lethargic and reluctant to go for a walk or move at all. In rare cases the dog may vomit. Treatment usually only provides a temporary relief of symptoms. Medication to improve the action of the heart and to remove excess fluid may help. In final stages it may be necessary to remove some of the fluid manually from the abdomen.

Balanitis

Inflammation of the tip of the penis and the sheath. Dogs with balanitis have a discharge of pus from the sheath. In practice this condition is so common that it is only treated when the discharge becomes a problem in the house or when the irritation distresses the dog. Local application of antibiotic creams alleviates the condition but rarely if ever effect a permanent cure.

Broken bones

See Fractures

Bronchitis

Inflammation of the bronchial tubes. Bronchitis rarely occurs on its own. It usually accompanies other infections of the respiratory system. The most important feature is a persistent and productive cough. It may develop from neglected cases of kennel cough. One form of bronchitis which may be encountered is that caused by migration of the young (larval) stages of worms through the lungs.

Bursitis

Inflammation of a bursa. A bursa is a fluid-filled pouch situated at various parts of the body to protect areas of friction from damage. They are sited where ligaments and tendons move over bone. Bursitis occurs most commonly in large dogs at the point of the elbow and the hock. Large, sometimes very large, swellings occur. Some cases appear painful although this is uncommon. Most cases are brought to veterinary surgeons when the swelling is very large or has ulcerated and become secondarily infected. Medical treatment may alleviate the condition but surgical removal of the area is usually a more definite solution.

Cancer

Cancer occurs when, for some reason which is not understood, some of the cells in the body change their characteristics and begin to divide uncontrolled, contrary to normal cell division. This new growth of tissue may grow very slowly where it begins and remain a discrete lump which can be easily removed. This is a benign tumour. Alternatively the cancer may grow very fast, infiltrate the surrounding tissue and interfere with its function. Worst of all some of these new cancerous cells may enter the blood stream to spread to other parts of the body where they continue to grow and divide, to produce secondary tumours. This type of new growth or cancer is designated malignant.

Because of the social stigma, and accompanying fear, of the word cancer many people are ignorant of the subject. There have been considerable advances in the methods of treating cancer in human patients. Many, many who would previously have died now recover, and survive to live normally into old age. Only the most malignant types of cancer continue to resist treatment.

Many of the methods of medical and surgical treatments of cancer are also used in veterinary medicine although economic limitations restrict the availability of some of the more sophisticated diagnostic and therapeutic apparatus.

Treatment of cancer can be divided into three broad approaches. Surgery is used to remove many types of benign cancer. The success of these cases is usually excellent. Surgery is also used to remove malignant cancer but there is always the danger that this type of tumour will recur in the same place or spread to other parts of the body. It may sometimes be necessary, economics permitting, to combine surgery with radiotherapy or chemotherapy.

Radiotherapy makes use of the fact that cancerous cells are more susceptible to, more likely to be killed by, radiation than normal cells. Chemotherapy, a very specialised and complicated branch of cancer therapy, uses drugs, or a combination of drugs, which have proved more lethal to cancer cells than normal cells.

Canine viral hepatitis

This condition is due to a virus infection which particularly but not exclusively affects the liver. It is a serious condition but a high proportion of infected dogs recover, the percentage being increased considerably by prompt treatment and good nursing.

There is a marked rise of body temperature, the dog becomes lethargic, refuses food and usually drinks considerable quantities of water. A severe conjunctivitis is rapidly complicated by secondary infection manifest by a purulent discharge. Afflicted dogs may vomit, occasionally have tonsillitis and usually show distress if touched close to the end of the ribs near the enlarged and painful liver. In some cases there may be jaundice. The condition is of short duration, most cases being satisfactorily concluded within ten days although a small percentage of dogs die.

Treatment aims at controlling secondary infection, controlling discomfort and protecting the liver from the ravages of the virus. Good nursing is essential.

A number of afflicted dogs develop a blue cornea some ten days after recovery. (See Eye disease) Most cases of blue eye – it can be in both eyes – clear satisfactorily but in a few cases the problem persists. There has been much concern over this phenomenon which can also occur after vaccination. Two types of vaccine are used to protect dogs against canine viral hepatitis, live attenuated and dead. The former occasionally produces the blue eye. While transient in most cases it can persist to become a disfigurement and presumably a problem to the dog although sophisticated sight testing is difficult in animals. Some breeds seem more susceptible to the effect than others. Veterinary advice should be sought when the puppy is given its initial course of vaccination.

Canker

This is a term with no special medical meaning in the dog. There is no specific condition of the ear to which it is applied. The fear it strikes among dog owners, probably because the name sounds like cancer, is totally without foundation. The very most it means is a disease of the ear. (See Ear disease)

Coccidiosis

A condition caused by small single-celled animals – protozoa – closely related to the amoeba of school biology fame. The condition is uncommon. Indeed many think that the coccidia are merely secondary opportunists which take advantage of a gut upset originating from other causes. A dog with enteritis in which coccidia are involved usually has severe diarrhoea which soon develops into dysentery showing blood and mucus.

Concussion

Damage to the brain tissue following a traumatic injury. May cause visual defects, behavioural disturbance and vomiting. Great care should be taken with concussed patients and they should be nursed with sensitivity. In severe cases there may be permanent mental disturbance.

Cruciate ligament rupture

While a number of ligaments are liable to be ruptured during an accident, the cruciate ligament is one of the most vulnerable.

Cruciate ligaments are two small crossed ligaments in the knee (stifle) between the femur and the tibia. (See Anatomy) They prevent a backwards and forwards movement of the two bones. These ligaments, particularly the anterior cruciate, may be ruptured. This may occur when the dog twists the knee although there is often no history of such an accident. The owner often sees nothing but the dog suddenly limping. Examination and X-rays are used to diagnose the condition. It is common to repair the condition surgically although if left many dogs are walking around in three months. Arthritis may follow cruciate rupture. Advocates of surgical repair believe the risk of arthritis is reduced if this treatment is used.

Cystitis

Inflammation of the bladder. Commoner in bitches than male dogs this condition is characterised by frequent urination with straining after urine is passed or squatting to the urination position without the passage of urine. There may be blood in the urine. Some afflicted animals show increased thirst. Treatment includes antibiotics, urinary antiseptics and increasing water intake by mixing water with food. The condition occurs in dogs of all ages, being not frequent in young bitches. It is very likely to recur.

Cysts

A cyst is a fluid-filled cavity with a lining membrane. Cysts occur in all parts of the body. They may be small or very large. Large cysts occur in the neck region causing considerable discomfort and disfigurement. Cysts may be drained of fluid but they usually recur unless the lining is destroyed. It is more effective to remove the cyst carefully, dissecting the lining membrane completely. (See Skin disease – Interdigital cysts)

Diabetes insipidus (water diabetes)

A rare condition of the pituitary body, a small but important endocrine gland housed within the brain. It produces excessive thirst and very frequent urination. The coat is often dry and appears in poor condition. There are often signs of dehydration. Treatment consists of injecting the hormone produced normally by the pituitary body which controls the loss of water through the kidneys. A cure is rarely possible but carefully managed and treated, afflicted dogs can live a normal life for many years.

Diabetes mellitus (sugar diabetes)

This condition is caused when the pancreas fails to produce sufficient insulin. Insulin, produced by special cells within the pancreas, essentially assists the body to make use of the carbohydrate, in the form of sugar, which is absorbed from the gut into the blood stream. Without insulin, the sugar cannot be used by the body. It is therefore excreted in large amounts through the kidneys. Because the body cannot use the food it eats, it lose weight and is in fact starving to death in spite of a plentiful supply of food.

Dogs with sugar diabetes have a voracious appetite, drink large quantities of water and urinate frequently. In the later stages they become lethargic, begin to vomit, may show constipation and difficulty with breathing. The condition is more common in bitches than in dogs. There is frequently the sweet smell of acetone by the body. A urine test is used to confirm the diagnosis.

There is no cure for sugar diabetes but dogs can often be maintained in reasonable health for many years with daily injections of insulin. Dietary control is also essential. Initially the dog has to be checked daily and the insulin administered by the veterinary surgeon. A careful check on the level of sugar in the urine must be kept. Once the correct dose has been ascertained the owner is taught to give the injection and to check the urine. Occasional checks are all that is then required by the veterinary surgeon.

Some dogs do not respond well to insulin therapy in which case euthanasia is the kindest solution. There are complications which arise in spite of insulin therapy. The commonest problem encountered is liver failure with possible jaundice and cirrhosis.

Dogs with diabetes then are well worth treating. They can often live quite happily with the condition for many years. Owners have to be prepared to collect frequent urine samples to monitor progress and to inject the dog daily.

Diaphragmatic hernia

A tear in the muscular sheet, the diaphragm, which separates the chest and the abdomen. It invariably results from a car accident. The main symptom is difficulty in breathing, the dog often assuming a sitting position. The diagnosis is confirmed by X-ray and the treatment is surgical repair.

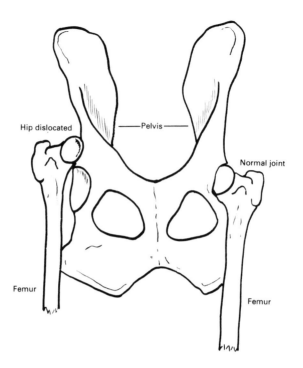

Hip dislocated — Pelvis —

Normal joint

Femur

Femur

Dislocation

Dislocation refers to a joint in which there is a loss of articulation. Dislocations may be total or partial. Commonly afflicted joints include the hip, shoulder, knee cap (patella), elbow and jaw. (See diagram)

Knee cap (patella) dislocations

This is one of the commoner dislocations. The knee cap or patella runs in a groove on the lower end of the thigh bone (femur). It is kept in place by a system of ligaments. The patella becomes dislocated when one of the collateral ligaments is torn in an accident. In most cases the outer collateral ligament is torn and the patella dislocates inwards. The dog with this injury has difficulty in walking and frequently holds the leg off the ground. Surgical repair of the torn ligament corrects the disability.

In some dogs, notably the toy breeds, the stifle is congenitally deformed. In this case the patella may be permanently dislocated from birth. Surgery may be used in some cases to improve the condition. Dogs with this affliction should not be bred from, but in practice the condition is so widespread in some breeds that one is hard pressed to find an example.

Distemper

Distemper and the closely related disease hardpad are caused by viruses. Until the advent of vaccination (see Part II, Vaccination) it was the scourge of dogs. A large percentage of puppies were killed or maimed by it.

Distemper occurs in three stages. Immediately after the infection there is a rise in the body temperature, the dog appears quite well although it may be less interested in food and may have a watery discharge from its eyes and nose. This stage lasts for only two or three days following which the temperature returns to normal and the dog appears to recover. In most cases owners do not seek veterinary advice at this stage assuming at worst only a mild condition.

The second phase begins a few days later with a second rise in body temperature and severe symptoms classical of distemper. There is a marked yellow discharge of pus from the nose and eyes. The eyes appear red. Breathing is often difficult, and is often accompanied by a cough. Vomiting and diarrhoea with or without blood is usual. Dehydration follows as a result of the vomiting and diarrhoea. In some cases, particularly puppies, pustules (small pus-filled swellings) appear on the belly and inner aspect of the thighs. The dogs at this stage are extremely lethargic and obviously distressed. The virus infection during this stage is always exacerbated by secondary bacterial infection and dogs which succumb and die during the second phase usually do so as a result of the secondary infection.

Clinical manifestations of the third stage of distemper are not inevitable. When they occur the outlook is often serious. They are due to nervous tissue damage by the virus. This stage may be seen several weeks after the second phase has apparently finished. The dog may well appear normal between the two stages although a slightly raised body temperature and mild intestinal upsets in the form of loose faeces sometimes persist. During this stage there may develop a very scurfy skin and the classic symptoms of hardpad in which the pads thicken to become rigid to the touch. During the third stage afflicted dogs may show evidence of nervous disease, irritation, poor co-ordination, fits, paralysis, uncontrolled pacing and coma. These symptoms, due to a severe encephalitis, often end in death. Occasionally mild nervous damage is seen in which groups of muscles 'twitch' (chorea) either continuously or when the animal is at rest. Mild forms of chorea may persist throughout life but appear not to inconvenience the animal. In some cases the chorea is severe and may necessitate euthanasia.

Distemper must always be considered a serious condition. There are no drugs at present available that negate the effects of viruses. Treatment concentrates on preventing the intervention of secondary bacterial invasion during the second stage of the disease, controlling the symptoms of gastro-enteritis and respiratory infection, rectifying the dehydration and generally nursing the dog to alleviate the misery. In most cases of third stage (tertiary) distemper, little can be done to save the dog although some of the modern anti-convulsant and anti-epileptic drugs may be of value.

Dysentery

Dysentery is essentially very severe enteritis with watery blood-stained diarrhoea. There are a number of causes and it requires immediate treatment. A closely related condition – haemorrhagic gastro-enteritis – is very sudden in onset, the dog shows persistent blood-stained vomiting together with blood-stained diarrhoea. An afflicted dog is rapidly weakened and may soon die. Owners have been known to leave an apparently healthy dog at night and wake to find an almost dead dog. The cause of the condition is unknown but because of its very sudden onset it is believed to be an allergic condition of the bowel. Treatment must be prompt if it is to have any chance of success.

Ear disease

Diseases of the ear are relatively common in the dog. They are manifest by apparent irritation or pain, the dog scratching or rubbing the afflicted ear, and often holding the head to one side. One or both ears may be affected. In many cases there is an accompanying discharge and associated smell. Inflammation of the ear canal (otitis externa) is caused by a number of agents. In certain parts of the country, and certain parts of the year, late summer and autumn, awns from wild barley cause considerable distress to dogs. Ear mites (See Otodectic mange, Parasitic skin problems under Skin disease) are a constant problem.

Various micro-organisms including bacteria, fungi, yeasts and viruses can cause problems either by themselves or as secondary invaders. Allergic reactions are suspected when there is a very sudden onset. General skin conditions may also cause trouble in the ear.

Grass awns are removed usually under a general anaesthetic not because it causes pain but because the dog is so acutely distressed it refuses to keep still. Ear mites are easily dealt with using appropriate parasiticides. Other causes must be dealt with using ointments and creams applied into the ear canal together with antibiotics and anti inflammatory drugs given by mouth or by injection. If the response is not rapid, i.e. if considerable resolution does not occur within a week, then careful cleaning of the canal under a general anaesthetic may be advised. Persistent or long standing ear disease is often successfully treated with surgery. The operation is designed to open the vertical canal thus improving both drainage and ventilation. This operation has a very high success rate, often relieving the condition completely.

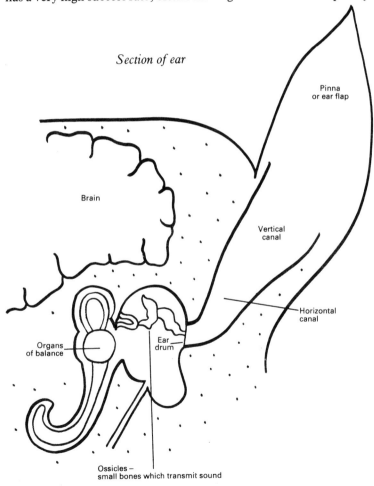

Section of ear

Pinna
or ear flap

Brain

Vertical
canal

Horizontal
canal

Organs
of balance

Ear
drum

Ossicles –
small bones which transmit sound

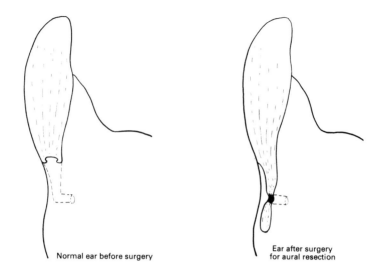

Normal ear before surgery

Ear after surgery
for aural resection

In rare cases, where thickening is severe, a more drastic operation for the total removal of the ear canal may be indicated.

Irritation of the ear canal causes the dog to shake its head often quite vigorously. This activity occasionally causes a blood vessel to burst and so the ear flap begins to swell. This is exactly the same problem which plagues professional fighters who sustain cauliflower ears. Provided the swelling is slight it can safely be left but if, as often happens, the swelling is severe then the ear has to be drained surgically. Whether left alone or opened there is likely to be a degree of crumpling.

Middle-ear disease (otitis media) is a serious condition affecting that part of the ear beyond the ear drum which contains also the organs of balance. Affected dogs may show severe distress, disturbed balance or circling. The condition needs prompt professional assistance.

Ear conditions cause considerable distress to the dog. As with most diseases correct diagnosis and proper treatment are essential if rapid resolution is to be achieved. Amateur meddling using patent medicines is unlikely to be effective. It simply prolongs the dog's agony, wastes time and expends money uselessly.

Encephalitis

Inflammation of brain tissue. It has a number of causes including infections – notably distemper – and various poisonous substances. Encephalitis may cause temperamental changes or fits. It is often diagnosed clinically but this can be confirmed with brain reading (electroencephalogram, EEG). Treatment depends on the cause but the condition should always be considered serious. (See Distemper, Rabies, Canine viral hepatitis)

Enteritis

Inflammation of the bowel. May or may not be accompanied by vomiting. (See Gastritis) The classic symptom of enteritis is diarrhoea. The dog may otherwise appear normal or it may be listless and dejected, refuse food and seek cool surfaces. If the disease continues the dog will become weak and dehydration will be evident. Enteritis has many causes including incorrect diet, poisons, corrosive substances, and infections. Professional assistance should never be delayed beyond twenty-four hours and sought sooner in young puppies. First aid treatment is to starve the dog and administer kaolin but this should never be continued beyond twenty-four hours without professional advice. Treatment depends on the dog's condition. Administration of saline by injection is often required in the moderate to severe cases.

Epilepsy

This condition is still not fully understood. For some reason there is electrical confusion in the brain. The normal electrical pathways are disorientated temporarily. When an attack occurs the dog loses consciousness, falls to the ground, and may twitch and froth at the mouth. The fit lasts from a few seconds to a few minutes. Following the attack the dog appears dazed, and may not seem to know where it is. During an attack owners should leave the dog alone and remove any objects close to it on which it is likely to damage itself. When it comes round a comforting word is helpful. **Do not** attempt to touch the dog or 'pull its tongue out'. You will get bitten. The condition can be confirmed with an EEG. Treatment is not possible. Many dogs are kept free of, or have reduced, attacks with the use of modern antiepileptic drugs. Treatment, like for human sufferers, has usually to be given daily.

Epistaxis

Epistaxis means bleeding nose. It is usually due to a blow but may accompany nasal infection or cancer of the nose and nasal sinuses. (See Sinusitis)

Epulis

A swelling of the gums which is benign cancer of the covering of the bone (periosteum). It has the same consistency and colour as normal gum. It can be removed and the area cauterised but this is usually only undertaken if the growth is large enough to prevent the dog eating or closing its mouth.

EYE DISEASE

The various diseases affecting the eye are grouped together for convenience. For conditions affecting the lids see Eyelid disease. Reference to the diagram will assist in understanding the text. Eye diseases are always serious and should always be dealt with by a veterinary surgeon.

Conjunctivitis

The eye is lined with a membrane, the conjunctiva. (See diagram) Conjunctivitis is an inflammation of that membrane.

It may be caused by an infection, in which case there may be a discharge of pus, or it may be due either to a physical or chemical agent which has damaged the eye. The afflicted eye will be red and painful. There is often a discharge of watery fluid or pus. The dog may rub the eye, tend to keep it closed, or appear distressed. Professional attention is essential.

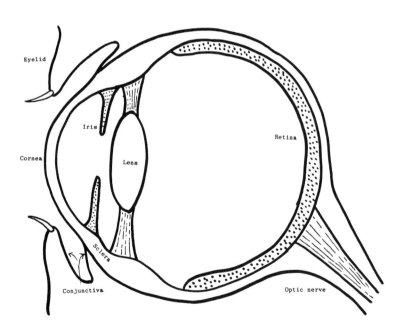

Eye

Blue eye

Two structures can if damaged give the eye a blue appearance. There are several causes for this but perhaps the best known is the damage due to the viral infection, canine viral hepatitis. There has been much national publicity particularly in the doggy press concerning the possible effect of live attenuated vaccine on the cornea. Certain breeds appear to be more susceptible than others.

The blue cornea may occur both following natural infection and after vaccination with the live vaccine. In most cases the effect is temporary but a few dogs have sustained permanent damage.

The second cause of a blue or bluish-white appearance to the eye is cataract. An eye is said to have a cataract when the lens, which is situated just behind the iris, degenerates causing it to become opaque. Cataracts are a feature of old age in many dogs. There is little in the way of medical treatment to retard progress of the cataract. Peeping through the opaque lens is probably like looking through frosted glass. Surgical removal of the lens, a commonly employed solution to the problem in man, is much more difficult in the dog for various technical reasons, and is far less commonly undertaken, indeed many veterinary surgeons are reluctant to employ surgery for cataracts.

Corneal ulcers

Corneal ulcers are painful breaks in the surface of the cornea. Affected dogs indicate their discomfort by rubbing, and tend to keep the eye partially closed. The third eyelid (nictitating membrane) is often partially across the eye. Corneal ulcers may be seen if deep, but very shallow ulcers can be stained to demonstrate the broken surface. Most corneal ulcers heal rapidly with topically applied eye ointment but persistent ulcers may need surgical treatment including chemical cauterisation to effect resolution. All breeds of dog are susceptible but the pop-eyed breeds like pugs and pekinese, are particularly prone. Ulcers can be caused by physical or chemical injury or result from nutritional deficiencies or infection. In rare cases the ulcer may continue to develop, it may deepen to penetrate the cornea, resulting in the loss of the eye.

Luxation of lens

In some breeds notably the wire haired fox terrier and the Sealyham there is a tendency for the lens to leave its moorings and lie partially or totally free in the eye. This may result in a number of secondary problems including conjunctivitis, corneal opacity and glaucoma. The condition requires that the lens be removed surgically.

Progressive retinal atrophy

The retina is that part of the eye which in analogy to a photographic camera corresponds to the film. It receives the picture. The condition is inherited. It usually becomes apparent to the owner during middle age, the dog first appearing blind at night. The pupils may be enlarged and there is often a mild conjunctivitis. Cataracts frequently complicate the condition and present difficulties for diagnosis which depends on examining the retina and the nerve at the back of the eye. Night blindness progresses to partial sight during the day and eventually to total blindness. There is no cure and nothing can be done to arrest the condition. Afflicted animals should not be used for breeding but since it is not apparent until after the conclusion of most dogs' breeding life only a national eradication scheme which follows the fortunes of several generations could hope to reduce the incidence of the disease. Such a scheme has been tried by the B.V.A. with the co-operation of the Kennel Club.

Glaucoma

Refers to an increase in the pressure inside the eye. It is not itself a disease but a symptom caused by several conditions. The condition in man is recognised by pain and some visual problems. In the dog these important early symptoms are unfortunately missed and the owner seeks professional help only when the condition is well advanced, the eye being obviously swollen. Increased pressure causes blindness and this has often occurred by the time veterinary help is sought. Treatment depends on the cause and the stage the condition has reached. Medical treatment, including the local application of drops, may control the condition. Surgical relief of the pressure may be necessary. It is sadly often necessary in the dog to remove the eye.

EYELID DISEASE

The eyelids have the important role of protecting the eye from damage. They close reflexly if anything approaches the eye, keep it covered during sleep and continually close across it – blink – during waking periods to ensure the surface is kept moist with tears and clean.

Entropion

A congenital condition of the eyelids in which they turn inwards over all or part of the lid. It may affect one or both lids, of one or both eyes. This condition is usually seen in young puppies although it can occur in older animals. Entropion causes considerable irritation, the afflicted animal may rub or paw the eye or eyes and there is usually a

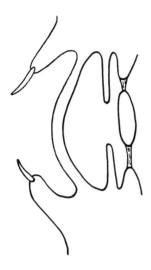

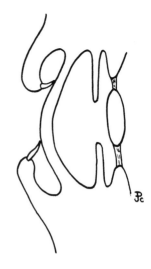

Normal eyelids   Entropion eyelids turned in. Eyelashes rub cornea

clear watery or purulent discharge. In neglected cases the cornea may be damaged. This distress, caused by the condition, in which hairs are constantly rubbing the sensitive eye, can be imagined. Since the condition is inherited serious doubts should be entertained by those contemplating breeding from affected animals. Although entropion can be corrected surgically with relative ease it must be a first principle to eradicate the condition by a sensible breeding programme. In practice the affliction is so widespread in some breeds – notably chows – that one would be hard pressed to find suitable breeding stock for such a programme. (See also Breeding)

Ectropion
A condition in which the eyelids are slack and droop to expose the sensitive conjunctiva. This is an inherited condition which causes afflicted dogs a great deal of discomfort. (See Entropion) The condition – classical in bloodhounds and common in spaniels, St. Bernards, Newfoundlands and Pyrenean mountain dogs – is unsightly and anatomically unsound. It can be surgically corrected but like entropion the aim should be to reduce the incidence of the condition by a breeding programme.

Trichiasis
A rare condition in which the eyelashes grow in the wrong direction and impinge upon the eyeball to cause considerable discomfort with rubbing, pawing and a watery discharge. Severe or neglected cases may cause damage to the cornea.

Distichiasis

More common than trichiasis. Afflicted animals have a double row of eyelashes. One grows normally while a second row originating from the edge of the lid, rubs against the cornea causing irritation and discomfort. Treatment depends on the severity of the condition. The lashes may be periodically plucked under a general anaesthetic, or if the condition is extensive and severe more radical surgery can be employed. Pekinese and poodles are often affected although it occurs in many breeds.

Wart on eyelid

It is not uncommon to see a small wart-like structure arising from the edge of the lid. These small structures, actually related to the glands of the lid, grow slowly in size and appear usually to cause mild irritation. If the lid is everted a 'root' can be seen descending from the edge to the deeper tissue. The treatment for this condition is surgical. Removal should be undertaken as soon as it is diagnosed. Delay will allow growth and since the operation requires a V-shaped section to be removed from the lid the smaller this section the less difficulty in closing the wound.

Harderian gland enlargement and prolapse

This is caused by a blockage of Harders gland, which is situated in the third eyelid (nictitating membrane). From the inner corner of the eye can be seen a red enlargement. The swelling rarely causes discomfort. Surgical removal is the most effective treatment.

Tear duct blockage

Tears are produced by the tear glands at the outer corner of each eye. They flush across the eye keeping it moist and clean and then drain into the tear ducts by two small holes at the inner corner. The ducts take the tears to the inner part of the nose. Humans are most aware of this process if they cry when because of the increased quantity of tears there is an accumulation in the nostril and there is a desire to blow one's nose. Occasionally the tear duct becomes blocked in one or both eyes which in turn causes the tears to overflow. In white dogs hair below the eyes stains brown. As a simple test of tear duct function one can drop stain into the eyes. This rapidly appears at the nostril in a normal eye as it is flushed down the ducts by the tears. If the ducts are blocked then the stain is either very slow to appear or does not appear at all.

A delicate technique exists to flush the blocked glands through. This is done under an anaesthetic not because the procedure is painful but because the dog must remain very still while it is accomplished.

Fractures

When a bone is broken it is said to be fractured. Several types of fracture occur. In young animals, including puppies, the bone is so soft and pliable that it may sustain a partial fracture which resembles the way a green stick breaks when bent. It is called a greenstick fracture. A simple fracture describes a bone broken completely across in one place. In a comminuted fracture the bone is broken into several pieces. Impacted fractures have one part of the fractured bone forced into the other. Compound fractures indicate an external wound at the site of the break.

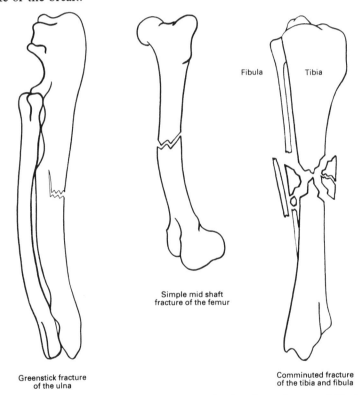

Fibula Tibia

Simple mid shaft
fracture of the femur

Greenstick fracture
of the ulna

Comminuted fracture
of the tibia and fibula

Traditionally broken bones are repaired using plaster of Paris applied externally. This remains a perfectly satisfactory method of immobilising the bone fragments while the repair takes place in a number of fractures.

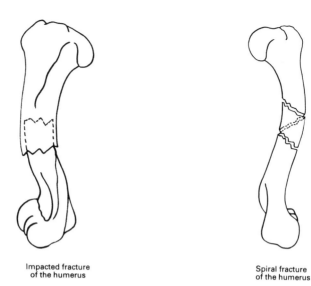

Impacted fracture
of the humerus

Spiral fracture
of the humerus

In many cases however plaster of Paris is unsatisfactory and to-day it is possible to use various internal metal supports to immobilise the bone. These may take the form of strong stainless steel pins, plates or screws. There can be no doubt that the application of these sophisticated methods of repair have greatly improved the results.

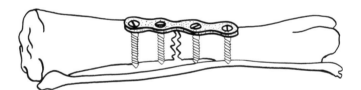

Repair of fractural tibia using a stainless steel
four-screw plate

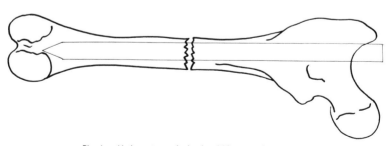

Pin placed in bone to repair simple mid fracture of the femur

When bone is fractured the body at first surrounds the pieces with a crude, soft bone which rapidly immobilises the pieces. This is called a bridging callus. Later the body trims this large rather bulky callus down and replaces it with harder more durable bone. If we have aligned the bone, either with plaster of Paris or internal metal appliances, before the bridging callus is laid down by the body the bone will be reasonably straight when the repair is complete. If not in line the body will still go ahead with the callus but the bone may well be crooked and the dog permanently lame.

Foreign bodies in the alimentary canal (gut)

Dogs have the most amazing habit of eating a wide variety of rubbish from nylon tights to rubber balls, pieces of wood and large pieces of bone to coins of the realm. In many cases these are passed without incident along with the faeces. Occasionally they are too large to make their way along the bowel. They cause a blockage which produces severe symptoms of intestinal obstruction. The condition will lead to death in a very few days unless surgery is undertaken for removal of the offending object.

The symptoms may be slow or rapid in onset. An afflicted dog vomits, is listless and dejected and is reluctant to move. It rapidly becomes dehydrated and there are either no faeces at all or only small amounts. The dog may be in considerable pain due to local peritonitis around the section of bowel containing the foreign body. Prompt professional help is essential.

Gastric distension and gastric torsion

These two conditions occur in large breeds of dog. They are both extremely serious and only prompt medical and surgical attention will save the dog's life. These conditions are real emergencies. The abdomen begins to swell and rapidly becomes tense like a drum. The dog is very distressed with shallow rapid breathing. It is in a state of severe shock. Many dogs with this condition try unsuccessfully to vomit. The cause of the condition is unknown but seems to be related to some combination of eating, drinking and exercise. It can be prevented to some extent by feeding several small meals a day rather than one large one. The condition is very likely to recur. Treatment depends on prompt surgery to open and empty the stomach. The difference between the two closely related conditions is rather academic. In gastric distension the stomach simply swells while in gastric torsion the stomach is twisted on its long axis.

Gastritis

Inflammation of the stomach. This condition can occur alone or may be accompanied by inflammation of the bowel, enteritis – thus gastro-enteritis. It has a multitude of causes including poisons, corrosive chemicals, foreign bodies such as stones or bones, and various infections due to numerous micro-organisms. Dogs suffering from gastritis usually show persistent vomiting. They may appear bright, but can often be dejected. Severe thirst is common where prolonged vomiting occurs, the vomit may contain blood. Vomiting is the body's method of ridding itself of noxious substances and may therefore save the animal's life. Prolonged vomiting is however extremely weakening, the body loses essential body salts along with the vomited fluids. This rapidly causes dehydration and severe shock. Prompt treatment is essential. As a first aid measure, do not allow the dog to feed. Allow only very small laps of cold boiled water and keep the dog warm. If the dog is suspected of eating a poisonous substance take the name of the poison or the packet in which it was contained to the veterinary surgeon along with the dog.

Gastro-enteritis

(See Enteritis and Gastritis)

Gingivitis

Inflammation of the gums. This may be a local condition and often accompanies paradontal disease. It is also a symptom of general infection. The gums appear red, are often sore, appear to be painful and may be swollen. They may bleed when touched, and there may be an offensive smell. Treatment will depend on cause, but antibiotics may be accompanied by local application of mild antiseptics.

Glossitis

Inflammation of the tongue. The tongue appears swollen and the dog may salivate. The condition is often due to bee or wasp stings and in this case the tongue should be examined for the sting and this removed. It should be seen by a veterinary surgeon since it may interfere with breathing and in rare cases can choke the dog. Swelling of the tongue is occasionally caused by a rubber band around the base.

Haematoma

A haematoma, commonly called a blood blister, is an accumulation of free blood in the tissue following a burst blood vessel. Haematomas

may occur following a blow to the body, from a car accident or kick. A commonly encountered haematoma follows head shaking which accompanies ear disease. The ear flap may swell alarmingly causing the dog considerable distress. Treatment depends on the position of the haematoma and its size. It is usual to leave well alone or simply apply cold compresses. In some cases of haematoma of the ear flap it is necessary to open the haematoma surgically to drain it.
(See Ear disease and Skin disease, Otodectic mange)

Haemorrhagic gastro-enteritis
(See Dysentery)

Hardpad
(See Distemper)

Heart disease
Heart disease is generally a condition of middle aged or old dogs although the emergence of the relatively new disease parvovirus has meant a marked increase in the number of puppies and young dogs with heart disease. There are many different conditions which can affect the heart, which require skill, experience and modern technology to distinguish. In many cases owners do not realise their dog has a heart affliction. Occasionally however they may present the dog at the surgery because it is listless, tires easily while out for a walk, has short fainting fits or a dry cough. Diagnosis of the condition may be possible by use of stethoscope or electrocardiogram (ECG). In general the heart is a stout and sturdy organ able to overcome many of its own deficiencies by increasing effort in several ways. The heart can be assisted considerably in disease by using drugs of various kinds.

Perhaps the greatest problem for the veterinary clinician treating a dog with heart disease is gaining the confidence of the owner. Since, in most cases, the owner has no way of knowing how bad the heart actually is, any improvement or deterioration observed by the veterinary surgeon will be equally obscure. Owners will be asked to administer pills to a dog which, to them, appears normal. Examinations to monitor the condition, and the drugs cost money for which there is little obvious return. In these circumstances owners have to rely on the trust and mutual confidence which they have established with their veterinary surgeon. Treatment of heart conditions is without doubt beneficial to the dog's welfare. In most cases treatment has to continue for the rest of a dog's life.

A check with a stethoscope confirms a sound heart in Fred

Owners are naturally concerned about the advisability of exercising a dog with a heart condition. A personal view, always expressed, is that if a dog isn't able to go for a walk, one of the most exciting parts of its day, then its life isn't worth prolonging. My advice is that exercise should continue as normal, except in periods of real cardiac crisis, the owners accepting the risk in the knowledge that if their dog were to die as a result it would die happy. Overprotection of canine heart patients by owners I believe to be a manifestation of selfishness.

One of the most common conditions affecting old dogs' hearts is mitral valve incompetence. Essentially, the valve separating the auricle from the ventricle on the left side of the heart fails to close, as it should, with each contraction of the heart. Thus, instead of the pressure created by the heart beat used to pump blood around the body, some of the blood is forced back into the auricle, creating a back pressure. Eventually a build up of fluid on the lungs occurs. This may cause the dog to cough.

Congenital heart conditions are rare in the dog but it is useful to have the heart examined soon after it is acquired just to be sure. Most veterinary surgeons examine puppies clinically when giving the routine vaccination. A heart examination of young dogs has become more important with the emergence of parvovirus. (See Parvovirus)

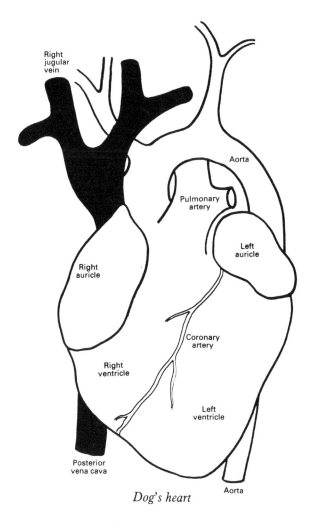

Dog's heart

Heat stroke
In the U.K. heat stroke is most commonly encountered when dogs are left in cars during warm weather. Temperatures within a closed car, standing in the sun, can rise very rapidly indeed. Dogs confined in such conditions become very distressed. Their body temperatures rise and, unless the condition is promptly reversed, they suffer irreversible brain damage and die. Affected dogs begin to pant, and have an anxious expression. They remain in a sitting or standing position until very near death.

Afflicted dogs should be placed in or covered with cold or iced water to reduce the body temperature and professional assistance enlisted without delay.

Hepatitis
Inflammation of the liver. The liver is a very complicated organ which fulfils a large number of bodily functions. Diagnosis of liver disease is complicated, often requiring a number of sophisticated laboratory tests. Hepatitis may be evidenced by a number of symptoms including vomiting and diarrhoea, lethargy, excessive thirst and pain behind the ribs. Some forms of hepatitis also produce a jaundice. Hepatitis has several causes. It may be due to poisons or infections. It is a very serious condition and must be treated professionally.
(See Canine viral hepatitis)

Hernias
Hernias occur when body contents pass through a hole in the body wall that should have closed but for some reason has not. By far the commonest hernias are umbilical, at the umbilicus or belly button and inguinal at the groin. When the contents pass through a tear in the body muscle it is called a rupture. To confuse the picture some so-called hernias are wrongly termed being in fact ruptures. The best example of this is the diaphragmatic hernia. (See Diaphragmatic hernia)

Inguinal hernia
An inguinal hernia appears as a soft swelling in the groin and can occur in both male and female. This occurs when abdominal contents pass through the potential opening between sheets of muscle in the inguinal or groin region. The testicles of the male pass through the gap when they descend from the abdomen during development. Normally the gap is closed and the contents of the abdomen, apart from the

testicles, are prevented from passing through it. In some cases however the closure is incomplete and loops of intestine, uterus even bladder may find its way through. Surgical repair is essential.

The danger of this, as in other hernias and ruptures, is that the loops of bowel caught through the opening may begin to swell with gas. This in turn causes the blood supply to be clamped off and the trapped loop of bowel, devoid of oxygen and nutrients, dies. This is termed a strangulated hernia. Strangulated hernias are hot, red, swollen and painful to the touch. Immediate surgery is essential if the dog's life is to be saved.

Perineal hernia

This condition is seen occasionally in old male dogs. It is in fact not a hernia at all. It appears as a large swelling to one side of the anus and occurs when, for some unexplained reason, the muscle tissue which supports the side of the rectum begins to waste allowing the side of the rectum to balloon. Faeces become trapped in the side pocket, or diverticulum. This large swelling in the pelvis causes the dog to strain but to no avail since the faeces cannot escape through the anus.

Treatment may be medical coupled with regular manual clearing of the diverticulum or a surgical repair may be undertaken to add support to the wall of the rectum. The condition is believed to be due to excessive straining caused by an enlarged prostate gland. It is therefore usual to examine and if necessary treat the enlarged prostate gland. In some cases this may include castration.

Umbilical hernia

This is a true hernia. Abdominal contents pass through a gap left in the body wall created by incomplete closure of the umbilicus at birth. The size of this hernia in the middle of the belly varies considerably. It may be very small and contain only a small piece of fat or very large, and contain considerable amounts of abdominal organs. In some cases the contents of the hernia will disappear into the abdomen and then drop through the hole again to cause the swelling. Treatment is surgical. Some small hernias may safely be left alone, untreated.

Hip dysplasia

The term 'hip dysplasia' incorrectly describes the condition for which it is used, but it is now so well established and in such common use that it is unlikely it will be changed. The condition is seen in all large breeds of dog, although it is best known and first described in the

Hip dysplasia

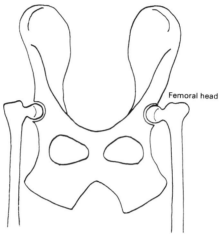

Femoral head

Normal hip joints showing deep round sockets
and well formed heads

alsatian. The symptoms are of varying degrees of lameness and instability of the hind legs. It is known to have a genetic factor but a national scheme run by the British Veterinary Association in conjunction with the Kennel Club has sadly failed to achieve the eradication which was originally anticipated.

The condition is often suspected clinically but diagnosis can only be confirmed and the degree assessed by X-ray examination. In many cases the condition can be treated medically but at times it is prudent and necessary to resort to surgery. Several operations for relief are possible. It is rarely necessary to destroy dogs for this condition except when severely crippled by secondary arthritis in old age. It is clearly unwise to breed from afflicted dogs. Certificates of suitability for breeding are issued by the B.V.A. through an owner's veterinary surgeon after examination of the X-ray photographs. Owners who wish to breed from one of the larger breeds are advised to consult their veterinary surgeon therefore before having their dogs mated.

Hydrocephalus

Means literally water on the brain. There are two types: external, in which the head is enlarged and deformed – this condition is rare – and internal, caused by a disorder of the drainage of fluid within the brain. Both cause behavioural disturbances. Internal hydrocephalus may be suspected by a clinician but is best confirmed by the use of a brain

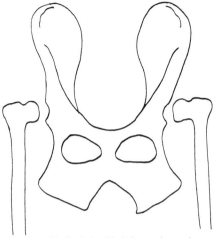

Severe hip dysplasia with shallow sockets and
poorly shaped femoral heads causing partial luxation

reading, EEC. Treatment is possible. Apart from occasional problems many afflicted dogs can lead a reasonable life. Surgery is used in man to correct hydrocephalus, but cost prohibits its use in dogs.

Intussusception

A very serious and acute condition which affects puppies. It is rare in older dogs. It is usually associated with severe diarrhoea and occurs when a section of the intestine telescopes into a section behind it. The puppy is in extreme pain, often cries out, shows severe pain to the touch, vomits and may show small amounts of watery or bloody diarrhoea. The puppy is obviously very sick. The intussusception can often be felt as a long sausage shape in the abdomen. Prompt attention and emergency surgery is essential.

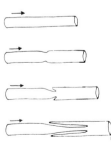

*Formation of
an intussusception*

Jaundice

Jaundice is strictly not a disease but a symptom. It is apparent in a dog because the body, including the skin, eyes, and inside of the mouth, becomes a bright yellow. The urine is also bright yellow. There are several causes for jaundice and it is described as obstructive, toxic, haemolytic or infective jaundice, depending on the cause. Jaundice indicates a very serious disease and professional assistance must be enlisted without delay. (See Hepatitis)

Kennel cough (Tracheobronchitis)

Kennel cough is most commonly seen in dogs which have been in kennels. It is due to an infective micro-organism but the effects of infection are doubtless exacerbated by persistent barking. Dogs with this condition rarely have a temperature and often do not appear unwell. The constant feature is a cough, which may be productive, a white froth being expelled through the mouth. The back of the throat is very inflamed and sore and is usually covered in white froth. The condition is very contagious, whole kennels becoming rapidly affected. It is often seen in summer as outbreaks. Kennel cough is not usually serious but is persistent and professional treatment is advisable. Occasionally complications occur. In addition to broad spectrum antibiotics it is often advisable to administer a mild cough mixture.

Labial folds

The condition, found in the loose lipped, heavy jowled breeds, like spaniels and setters, can produce the most appalling smell which pervades the whole house, can lose you friends and even precipitate divorce!

The labial folds are two small indentations about halfway along the lower lips. The folds become thickened, raw and infected. Medicines and ointments may relieve the condition but surgical removal of the folds is a simple operation which will clear the condition permanently.

Laryngitis

Inflammation of the larynx. A rare condition in the dog. Loss of voice or altered quality to the bark is a common factor of the disease and the dog may cough. It is most often seen in dogs from kennels, which have alleviated their boredom and frustration by giving voice. Altered voice is a feature of rabies.

Leptospirosis

Two closely related bacteria (leptospira icterohaemorrhagica and leptospira canicola) cause the disease in the dog. Both also afflict man. The condition has therefore some public health significance. Fortunately protection against both conditions is now routine, being part of the normal vaccination programme recommended for all dogs. (See Part II, Vaccination) Leptospirosis is a very severe and unpleasant condition which frequently ends in death. Affected dogs refuse food, have a considerable thirst and vomit. They rapidly become dehydrated, lose weight, are very lethargic and reluctant to move. In some cases blood is seen in the vomit. Diarrhoea is common and may also include blood. In many cases there is a high temperature. In the later stages the eyes may have a glassy sunken appearance and they will have a watery or purulent discharge. Many dogs resent being touched because of painful abdominal organs, the liver and kidneys being primary sites for infection. Some cases of leptospirosis show jaundice. In the later stages of the disease there may be ulcers in the mouth and blood stained saliva may dribble from the mouth. Damage to the kidneys' function is reflected by the passage of only small amounts of very dark urine.

Treatment depends on killing the bacteria with antibiotics, together with symptomatic treatment of the damage done to the animal. This includes the injection of fluids and drugs to protect and repair the liver and kidneys.

Mammary tumours

Mammary tumours are reasonably common in the middle aged and older bitch. Fortunately the majority are benign. They may be detected as small hard peas in the mammary glands. Many mammary tumours increase in size after a heat period, clearly suggesting the hormonal control which is exerted by the ovaries. If left untreated they may become very large and pendulous. Eventually they may ulcerate at some point on their surface to produce a continuous, sometimes offensive-smelling discharge. In most cases mammary tumours are best removed as soon as they are identified. Many veterinary surgeons advise owners to spay the bitch as well, in an attempt to prevent recurrence of new tumours forming in other glands.

Surgical removal is the treatment of choice. In some cases the tumour alone is removed while it may be necessary to perform a mammary strip in which case the mammary glands on one side are removed in one operation.

Mastitis

Inflammation of the mammary glands. Mastitis most frequently occurs while the glands are producing milk. (See Part II, Breeding) They become infected and are very swollen, red and extremely painful. The condition can occur at other times and may be due to physical damage. In most cases the bitch will refuse food, be dejected and will have a raised body temperature. Bathing the glands with warm water together with antibiotics usually alleviates this serious condition.

Meningitis

Inflammation of the meninges, the covering of the brain and central nervous system. It is very rare in dogs. When it occurs there are often symptoms of severe pain in the back, behavioural changes and disturbed vision.

Metritis

Inflammation of the uterus. Due usually to infection of the uterus from outside. It is most commonly seen following whelping where hygiene has not been adequate or where an afterbirth has been retained. Bitches usually refuse food, have an increased thirst and a high temperature, and have poor milk yield if feeding pups. Treatment consists of antibiotics. A serious condition both for the bitch and her pups, which must be treated promptly.

Myositis

Inflammation of the muscles. This is an uncommon condition with many causes. Pain is evidenced in a reluctance to move, stiffness or signs of lameness. Treatment consists of rest, good nursing, physiotherapy and the use of cortisone and its derivatives.

A specific myositis of obscure origin, called cosinophilic myositis, is seen very rarely, associated with certain muscles of the head. An afflicted dog may have difficulty eating, may dribble saliva, and show swelling of the head muscles and eyelids. The condition tends to recur in spite of treatment. Eventually the muscles become wasted.

Nephritis

Inflammation of the kidney. This condition is always extremely serious. It may occur suddenly in dogs of all ages as a result of infection. The body temperature may be raised. Dogs with nephritis appear depressed and dejected, they usually refuse all food, have severe thirst and may vomit. They produce small quantities of very dark, often cloudy, urine and respond painfully to being touched on the back. Except in the very early stages they are dehydrated. Leptospirosis is a common cause of this condition.

Older dogs may develop a less acute form of nephritis but none the less serious for its slower onset. Old dogs with chronic nephritis may appear thin, often have poor appetites, classically have a severe thirst and frequently vomit. They are often very dehydrated. Afflicted dogs urinate a great deal, the urine being pale and voluminous. As the disease progresses they become dejected and rarely move. There is usually a characteristic fishy smell to the breath. Treatment is difficult, and is directed at dealing with the infection, giving fluids to rehydrate the dog and attempting to restore function to the damaged kidneys. Each case has to be treated individually. Diet is often an essential feature of treatment.

Neuritis

Inflammation of the nerves. A rare but severe condition in the dog. A nerve at any part of the body may be afflicted. The dog usually indicates the presence of the condition by biting and licking the area supplied by the nerve to the point of mutilation. Pekinese dogs have a specific problem in which they chew and bite their tail savagely. In some cases the effects are so severe that only amputation of the tail will relieve the animal's torment. Local neuritis may cause the dog to lick large areas of skin until they are devoid of hair and wet and suppurating. Neuritis is a very distressing condition. Veterinary attention should be sought.
(See Moist eczema)

Nymphomania

A very rare condition in the bitch. A constant bloody discharge is present, due usually to persistent or cystic follicles in the ovary. The most effective treatment is removal of the offending ovaries when the bitch is spayed.

Orchitis

Inflammation of the testicle. The testicle or testicles swell, are very hot, red and painful. The condition may be due to an external force or to infection. Antibiotics are essential.

Osteomyelitis

Infected inflammation of the bone. Before antibiotics the condition was extremely serious. In many cases limbs were amputated to save life. To-day, while still serious, recovery is the rule.

Pancreatitis

Inflammation of the pancreas. The pancreas is a complicated structure composed of two quite different tissues with two quite different and unrelated functions. The so-called internal products of the pancreas are absorbed by the blood. Their function is to assist the body to make use of its blood sugar. Failure of this part of the pancreas to work correctly causes sugar diabetes. (See Diabetes mellitus) The external products of the pancreas are passed along a tube and enter the intestine at the duodenrum. These products help the body to digest its food. We are concerned here with failure of the external products.

There is a rare but severe form of pancreatitis when the organ becomes suddenly swollen and painful. Afflicted dogs show severe gastro-enteritis and are acutely ill. More common is the slow form where the pancreas fails to produce its digestive aids normally. The dog loses weight, shows persistent or occasional diarrhoea, or rather greasy faeces. The condition may be temporary but is usually permanent. Treatment consists giving tablets and capsules containing the digestive juices the dog is failing to produce itself. The response to treatment is often dramatic. Faecal samples are usually sent to the laboratory to confirm the veterinary surgeon's clinical suspicion.

Parvovirus

Very recently a new disease afflicting dogs has emerged. Parvovirus is closely related to the virus which causes infectious feline enteritis (panleucopaernia) in cats. Indeed it is believed by some authorities to be a mutant form of the cat virus which has adapted to dogs. The condition has been causing distress with reported epidemic outbreaks in some districts. Fortunately vaccination against the disease is now possible and is likely to become a routine feature of puppy vaccination. The disease has two distinct effects on dogs depending on the age at which they contract the disease.

If puppies contract the disease within the first few weeks of life there is a very real chance of their succumbing. Indeed whole litters have died as a result of infection. In those puppies which survive there is a possibility that they will show symptoms of heart disease due to damage of the heart muscle by the virus. Personal experience of these cases suggest that many respond to treatment initially but it is still far too early to predict the long term effect on the heart.

Older puppies and adult dogs show severe enteritis or gastro-enteritis. Afflicted dogs become ill suddenly and rapidly collapse. Supportive treatment must be instigated promptly. While puppies and younger adults are most seriously affected there have been deaths in quite old dogs.

Treatment depends on the symptoms. In young puppies with heart involvement, careful treatment appears to produce at least partial recovery. In older dogs with symptoms of gastro-enteritis, treatment is aimed at alleviating symptoms and includes the use of injected fluids to combat the dehydration and shock caused by the rapid onset and severity of the disease.

Peritonitis

Inflammation of the peritoneum, or the layer of tissue which lines the abdomen and the intestines. Peritonitis is best known in man where it occurs as a consequence of a burst appendix. It is often caused in the dog following a wound from outside, including an infected surgical wound, or from a foreign body penetrating the gut from within. Dogs with peritonitis have a high temperature, vomit and the abdomen is extremely painful to the touch. Afflicted dogs seem anxious, are reluctant to sit or lie down and stand with an arched back. Peritonitis is a very serious condition requiring prompt professional attention and good nursing.

Pharyngitis

Inflammation of the pharynx or back of the throat. This is usually accompanied by both tonsillitis and laryngitis. The throat is red and painful. Dogs may cough, show salivation and make licking movements. They may go off their food, often have difficulty in drinking and appear depressed. Mild upper respiratory infection of all kinds may produce pharyngitis. It is a feature of kennel cough and distemper. Treatment depends on cause but will often include antibiotics. Mild cough syrups including honey are useful in relieving the symptoms.

Pleurisy

Inflammation of the pleural membranes, the membranes covering the inside of the chest cavity and the lungs. Dogs with this condition show severe breathing difficulties, appear very dejected and in great pain. They often sit upright and have their elbows out. Patients with pleurisy usually have a short dry cough. The body temperature is often very high. This is fortunately quite a rare condition in the dog. It can be treated successfully but prompt attention is essential. It is caused by a number of infective agents and by accidental damage to the chest.

Pneumonia

Inflammation of the lungs. Dogs with pneumonia have considerable difficulty in breathing. They often appear distressed. They usually prefer to sit up or lie on their chest. The respiratory or breathing movements are exaggerated. There are several causes of pneumonia. Several infections may settle in the lungs. In these cases there is a raised temperature, discharge from the nose and sometimes a productive cough. Dogs with pneumonia are often reluctant to eat either because of the effects of the concurrent infection or because eating requires some interference with breathing, which is already difficult.

Inhalation pneumonia results from the inhalation of fluids into the lungs. It usually results from the well-intentioned but inept administration of liquids to an uncooperative dog by an owner.

Parasitic pneumonia is caused by the migration of worm larvae through the lungs as part of their normal life cycle. The larvae pass from the intestine first to the liver and then by way of the blood stream to the lungs where they may cause severe inflammation. The much publicised toxocara canis, a common roundworm of the dog is one offender.

Poisoning

The number and complexity of poisonous substances are now legion. It would be quite impossible to list all poisons, together with their symptoms. Suffice to say that the sudden onset of symptoms in an otherwise healthy dog may indicate the presence of a poison and should prompt owners to seek professional help without delay. While some poisons have a slow insidious build-up within the body, the majority of common poisons either produce severe symptoms of gastro-enteritis with vomiting and diarrhoea, or nervous symptoms including excitability, incoordination, staggering or coma.

The treatment obviously depends on the poison and on the symptoms it produces. In some cases there are specific antidotes so it is always of great help when treating a patient for the veterinary surgeon to know the poison. If possible therefore take either the container and the name of the substance or some of the substance itself for analysis. If the poison is unknown it may be possible for the veterinary surgeon to identify it from the symptoms. Failing that the patient will be treated according to the symptoms it is showing and a specific antidote administered.

Prostatic hyperplasia

Enlargement of the prostate. All old male dogs have some degree of enlargement of the prostate, a sex gland surrounding the urethra, which produces some of the seminal fluid. However severe enlargement will cause difficulty in passing faeces and/or persistent straining. Difficulty in passing urine, the common feature of the disease in man, is rare. The condition is confirmed by rectal examination and by X-ray. Treatment is medical, although surgery is a possible, though little used, alternative.

Prostatitis

Inflammation of the prostate. This is far less common in the male dog than enlargement of the prostate. (See Prostatic hyperplasia) The dog refuses food, may vomit and shows severe abdominal pain particularly when touched. The body temperature is often high. Antibiotics are used in treatment.

Pyloric stenosis

A very uncommon condition caused by the failure of the muscle which controls the exit from the stomach to the intestine to open correctly. Dogs with this condition are rarely very ill and the vomiting occurs irregularly, usually when the animal is excited. The vomit is produced in an explosive fountain, called 'projectile vomiting'. The treatment is usually to surgically sever the offending muscular band.

Pyometritis

Pyometritis means a purulent inflammation of the uterus. It usually occurs in bitches over seven years of age. While it can occur in any unspayed bitch it is less likely in one that has had several litters. A single litter does not significantly reduce the chance of affliction.

The condition characteristically occurs either immediately after the heat period, when owners notice that a vaginal discharge continues after the normal three week span and that it becomes rather thicker, often foul smelling and yellow, or it occurs some two months after the conclusion of the heat. The symptoms are often of a very sick dog. The bitch may refuse food, drink excessively, vomit and become seriously dehydrated. The belly may become bloated and pendulous. There may or may not be a vaginal discharge depending on whether the cervix is open or closed. In general a closed cervix predisposes more severe symptoms. Body temperature usually rises. The diagnosis is straightforward in open cervix cases, but can be obscure when the cervix is closed. X-rays and blood samples may assist diagnosis in difficult cases. In very rare cases, notably in older animals, antibiotics may produce temporary regression but the treatment of choice is to remove the ovaries and uterus surgically. While surgery is often successful the operation must be considered to have a high risk and some bitches rapidly decline and die following surgery. The cause of death in these cases is often concurrent liver or kidney disease.

Rabies

Rabies is a world wide disease affecting all warm blooded animals including man. It therefore has considerable public health importance. Great Britain has been free of the disease for over fifty years. The strict quarantine laws are designed to keep it that way. In recent years a wave of the disease has spread across Europe to Northern France and is now close to the channel ports. It clearly threatens to cross the channel if vigilance is relaxed. The most likely method of entry will be through the auspices of a smuggled dog which is itself incubating the disease. (See Part II, Import of dogs to the U.K.)

Rabies is caused by a virus which attacks the nervous tissue. The symptoms of rabies vary considerably but are essentially all changes in behaviour. It is contracted by being bitten by a rabid dog or other animal.

The particularly unpleasant aspect of rabies is the very variable length of time from the infected bite to the time symptoms are apparent. This can be as little as two weeks but can be well over six months even up to a year in extreme cases.

The first signs of disease are changes in behaviour. Dogs during this phase of the disease may become unusually friendly where they were aggressive before, and may seek seclusion hiding under tables and beds. They may seem restless, barking at the slightest provocation. Some affected dogs make reflex snapping movements at imaginary flies. At this stage food and water may be taken normally or there may be some reluctance to eat. It is not unusual for the infected bite to be particularly irritant, the dog biting or scratching the area. Most dogs salivate at this point, the saliva being particularly infective. Attempts to restrain or hold the dog may result in being bitten. This first stage lasts for up to three days.

The second stage of rabies may take one of two forms, dumb or furious rabies. In both forms there is salivation, conjunctivitis, a yellow discharge from the eye and the third eyelid partially covering the eye.

Dumb rabies is characterised by an increasing paralysis. Paralysis of the facial muscles causes the jaw to hang down and give a sad, despondent look to the face. Paralysis prevents the dog from eating or drinking. The mouth becomes dry and the tongue brown. Paralysis of the throat muscles and vocal cords produce a characteristic change of voice, with a lowered pitch. When the dog stands it sways from side to side. It appears restless and will continue, as in the first stage, to snap at imaginary flies. The animal appears gaunt, with a dry dull coat. As death approaches the animal lies down all the time, stirring only if roused. The increasing paralysis affects the chest muscles and the breathing becomes slow and deep. Death relieves the agony after three or four days.

Alternatively the second stage may take the form of uncontrolled irritability, a furious dementia – furious rabies. The form favoured by film and fiction writers. In this form the dog is driven by some inner motivation. It has a frightened anxious expression. It travels considerable distances only stopping or deviating if something obstructs its path. Unlike dumb rabies dogs with the furious form can drink and eat, indeed they have a depraved appetite, chewing anything that comes their way. Eventually paralysis intervenes. The hind legs are affected first and followed by the muscles of the forelegs and body. Dogs die usually within two days.

The really terrible feature of rabies is the long incubation period. Anybody bitten by a dog in a country in which rabies is found has a very long period – up to a year – to know if rabies will develop. Injections designed to prevent rabies developing after a suspected bite are painful and unpleasant and there is no guarantee they will be effective. The virus present in infected saliva, and remember saliva is infected before clear symptoms of the disease are present, can gain entry to the body through a very small skin abrasion. An obvious bite is not essential.

We are very fortunate in Great Britain to be free of this horrifying disease. Strict application of the quarantine regulations are inconvenient to a few but are absolutely essential if we are to have any chance of remaining free from rabies. People who refuse to observe the regulations are socially and criminally irresponsible. The Rabies Act 1974 designates the imposition of severe penalties for smuggling dogs, or other animals subject to rabies control, into this country. If our vigilance is relaxed or our restrictive ramparts breached then our country will be the poorer.

Radial paralysis

The radial nerve supplies muscles of the fore leg. It is occasionally damaged in accidents, resulting in the dog being unable to move the leg forward. Afflicted dogs therefore drag the leg as they walk. In rare cases there may be recovery but all too often the condition is permanent. All except the heaviest breeds of dog can live reasonably happily with the problem so long as common sense nursing procedures are diligently pursued to prevent the foot becoming injured as it is dragged along.

Rectal obstruction

Rectal obstruction is evidenced by the classical sign of a dog straining but failing to pass faeces. The cause is either very dry faeces in the rectum, ground bone mixed in the faeces or a foreign body which having negotiated the convolutions of the bowel for some reason becomes stuck with success in sight. Treatment may include enemas and manual manipulation with or without a general anaesthetic.

Rectal prolapse

A rare condition of puppies. Due to excessive straining, usually associated with diarrhoea, part of the rectum everts. It appears as a blood red meaty swelling at the anus. It is quite serious. The dog is anaesthetised and the prolapse replaced. The anus is stitched with a purse string suture to prevent it coming out again.

Rhinitis

Inflammation of the lining of the nose. It accompanies most infections of the upper respiratory tract and also occurs in distemper. The main symptom is a nasal discharge which may be watery or contain pus.

Rickets

Rickets is due to a lack of vitamin D. This in turn interferes with the balance of calcium and phosphorus in the body. The condition, seen in young animals, may cause severe lameness in which limbs are bowed and the joints swollen. Vitamin D together with a carefully balanced mixture of calcium and phosphorus administered under professional supervision is essential.

Roundworms

In recent years, what may be described as an avalanche of irresponsible journalism has bombarded the public with tales of the dangers of roundworms, carried by dogs, causing blindness for man and particularly for children. The statistical reality is that the chances of damage from worms are so remote as to be unworthy of consideration. Forget it. The hysteria has been concocted by unscrupulous journalists in pursuit of a good story and the visual effect of wriggling worms on any television screen is guaranteed to increase viewing ratings. Needless to say it is a wise owner that ensures a regular worm programme for their dog.

Several types of roundworm exist, of which the most publicised is the toxocara species. A dog picks up worms by mouth (puppies may become affected while still in the womb) the eggs or infective larvae (young stage worms) pass to the intestine of the dog. From here they work their way through the intestinal wall into the blood stream, arrive at the lungs through which they migrate, to be brought up into the mouth and then swallowed back into the intestines as adults to live out their uninvited life.

In puppies the symptoms can be severe. Afflicted puppies may show a swollen belly with a generally poor condition. They may have diarrhoea or constipation, be very thin and lethargic. Puppies may have a cough or breathing difficulties caused by the migration of larvae through the lungs. Adults rarely show symptoms of infection although some cases of unthriftiness and poor coat may be attributed to roundworms.

Roundworms are easily treated. It is much better to approach your veterinary surgeon for a programme of worm treatment or control than to buy patent medicines.

Sinusitis

Inflammation of the head cavities known as sinuses. There is nearly always a discharge from the nose with sinusitis. It may be watery, blood stained or contain pus.

There are several causes of this condition. Treatment will depend on the cause.

SKIN DISEASE

Skin diseases could with justification be described as the veterinary surgeon's nightmare. They are, particularly in the summer months, one of the most frequent reasons an owner contacts a veterinary surgeon, and they present one of the most exacting tests of one's diagnostic ability. The skin not only suffers from its own localised conditions but has an unfortunate habit of reflecting various long standing conditions in other parts of the body. The skin has a very complicated structure reflecting its many duties which include protection, heat regulation, elimination of waste products in the sweat and awareness of the body's environment through touch.

We have seen under 'Symptoms' earlier that skin disease manifests itself in various ways. There may be hair loss, dry coat, scurf or dandruff, redness, irritation to produce licking or scratching, thickening wet secretion, watery vesicles or pus-filled pustules.

The diagnosis of skin disorders is complicated and time consuming. One of the problems for veterinary dermatology (the study of skin and its diseases) is the small amount of money available for research in this less than glamorous field of study and the consequent lack of sufficient specialists. While most skin problems can be solved quite quickly there are a number whose persistence tries the patience of owners and veterinary surgeons alike. The only advice which makes sense for frustrated owners is to have patience, and not to demand or expect instant cures. Many skin treatments take several weeks to become effective or apparent. If after a reasonable time you feel that there really is no progress than ask to see a skin specialist normally working from one of the veterinary schools.

Skin conditions can be grouped under various headings depending on their cause. The discussions here will be brief concentrating on the general problems encountered in skin disease.

Parasitic skin diseases

Parasitic infections of the skin account for a very high proportion of skin disease. Parasites infecting the dog's skin may be insects such as fleas and lice or arachnids (which have four pairs of legs and are related to spiders) including the various parasitic mange mites.

The majority of parasitic skin conditions, indeed the majority of skin conditions, are due to fleas. In the summer the flea population explodes and representative individuals seem to find their ways to most dogs. Fleas are very difficult to eliminate because the young larval forms develop off the dog, in the carpet and between floor boards under the dog bed. The larvae feed on the faeces of the adult flea which drops from the dog to the floor. The faeces contain a high proportion of partially digested dog blood. After three moults the larvae pupate. When the young adult emerges from the pupal case it re-infects the dog. The time taken for completion of this life cycle depends on a number of factors including the temperature and humidity. The cycle can be completed in about a month or may in cold unsuitable conditions extend for up to six months. Adults can live for many months.

Fleas bite their host dog with formidable mouth-parts and consume large quantities of blood. The flea bite is very irritating and will cause the dog to scratch. The scratching damages the skin causing extensive dermatitis (inflammation of the skin). In some cases dogs are actually

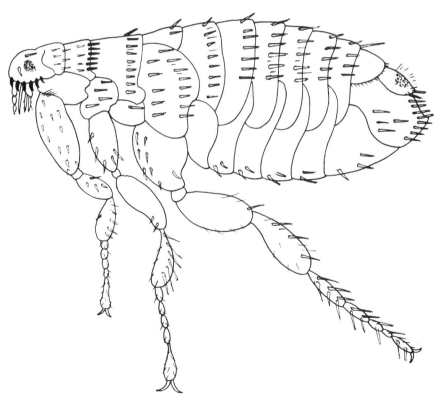

Dog flea (ctenocephalides canis)

allergic to fleas. In this case the reaction is extremely severe. The dog is often very distressed and the skin appears very red. There will be a degree of hair loss and broken hair and the skin may appear damp. Fleas also act as a secondary host for the common tapeworm of the dog. (See Tapeworms)

Eradication of fleas is far from the simple problem many people believe. The secret of the problem lies in the life cycle. Since the young live off the dog, the problem has to be tackled in two areas. The dog must be continually treated for long periods, since we have seen the young can take several months to develop. The dog will only remain clear if its coat is unsuitable for the young adult's survival when it climbs aboard. Treatment consists of flea powders, sprays, baths and tablets, repeated at regular intervals. The second front attacks the young fleas. Frequent changes of the dog bed, and frequent and diligent application of the vacuum cleaner, particularly to the area of the dog bed, removes the young physically. It is advisable to change bedding and vacuum the area each time the dog is treated for fleas. Finally if desperation intervenes the Local Authority will spray the house. While this may seem an extreme measure it is often the only course and the disruption is far less than might be imagined, nor is the cost prohibitive. Tablets are available for treatment as are flea collars impregnated with drugs which kill fleas.

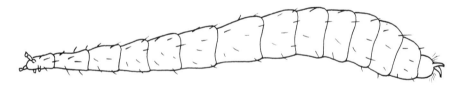

Flea larva

Lice

Lice are insects. There are two types, biting lice and sucking lice. They cause intense irritation and considerable distress to the dog. Adults cement their eggs, called nits, to the hair. The eggs are particularly resistant to applications which kill adult lice. The young hatch in about ten days and closely resemble their parents. They grow rapidly, moult three times and are fully mature in two' weeks. Lice once identified are relatively easily dealt with since the entire life cycle is completed on the host dog. Medicated baths, suitable for the destruction of lice must be applied every week to ten days.

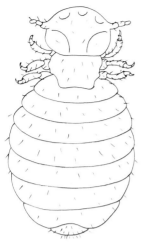

Biting louse (2 mm in length)   *Sucking louse (2 mm in length)*

Sarcoptic mange

Mange mites are related to the spiders. There are several types of mange. Sarcoptic mange is caused by the mite sarcoptes scabei. Adult mites lay their eggs in tunnels burrowed into the skin. It takes only fifteen days from egg to adult.

The condition is very serious although these days can be successfully treated. Damage to the skin causes intense irritation. The consequent scratching damages the skin, spreads the mites, and allows secondary bacteria entry to exacerbate the condition. Treatment consists of suitable medical baths.

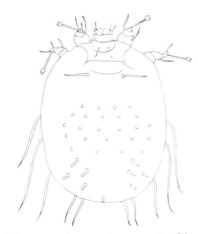

Sarcoptes scabei, cause of sarcoptic mange (scabies in man)
microscopic in size

Demodectic mange

Demodectic mange is caused by a very distinctive, cigar-shaped mange mite, demodex solliculcrum. This particular form of mange is very difficult indeed to treat. The condition shows hair loss, red or thickened skin. Sometimes irritation is intense and there may be secondary infection causing pustules. Various treatments exist but success is variable and relapses often occur. Treatment by mouth has been of some value in recent years.

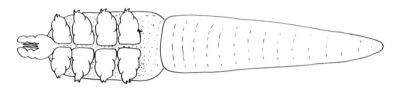

Demodex canis, cause of demodectic mange. Size 0.25 mm long (microscopic)

Otodectic mange

This is dealt with here because the mite (otodectes cynotis) is related to the skin mite but it is a condition affecting the ear. Adult mites lay their eggs in the wax of the ear. The eggs hatch in ten days. The mites which can just be seen with the naked eye march around the ear canal, sometimes in formidable armies. They feed on the skin lining the ear. Their saliva causes intense irritation. Some animals are extremely distressed by this infection and in rare cases may have fits. This mite infects both dogs and cats so if one animal in the household is affected, all animals of both species should be treated simultaneously every week with the application of suitable drugs dropped into the ear canal.

Ticks

Ticks are also related to the spiders. In some countries ticks carry diseases which they inject into their dog host incidentally when they pierce the skin to suck blood. In the U.K. the tick is not a carrier (vector) of disease. Ticks have an uneven distribution in the U.K. being most common in Cornwall and Devon, Wales, Scotland and in Northern Ireland. There are several types of tick which appear as moderate to large bodied creatures being brown or grey in colour. The common sheep tick resembles a castor bean. They are removed quite easily by covering them with a small wad of cotton wool covered in a noxious substance – methylated spirits or ether are commonly used – until they release their hold. The site of the wound made by their mouth-parts may become infected with bacteria so should be kept clean and carefully watched.

Hormonal skin problems

The endocrine glands of the body have complicated and far reaching effects on the body. Several kinds of skin problem are associated with disturbances of their normal balance and function. Diagnosis of these conditions is often very difficult and is complicated by the fact that they combine together or with other causes, for example secondary bacterial infection, to produce their effect. Redness, irritation, thickened skin, excessively waxy skin, dry coat and loss of hair may all be associated with hormone inbalance.

Bacterial skin problems

Some of the more severe problems are due to the invasion of very infective bacteria. These conditions usually respond well to antibiotics. In a large number of skin conditions bacteria are secondary invaders which jump on the bandwagon of a skin already weakened from another cause to make the condition even more severe and intractable. When treating these conditions it is important to remember that the original cause must also be considered.

Fungal skin problems

Fungi are a large group of parasitic plant-like organisms of which the mushroom and toadstool are free living examples. The commonest and most well known fungal infection is ringworm, a very infectious and extremely irritating skin condition. Athlete's foot in man belongs to this group of skin diseases. Previously these conditions were extremely difficult to treat. To-day there are specific drugs related to the antibiotics which are very effective in treating them. Diagnosis of these conditions depends on clinical appraisal, examining under a special form of ultra violet light and laboratory tests.

Allergic skin problems

Allergic skin conditions occur in dogs as they do in man. Our understanding of the allergic response has increased greatly over recent years. Identification of specific antigens which cause hay fever is now a well established branch of human medicine. In animals the cost of such complicated diagnostic tests prohibits their general use. We do however recognise a number of allergic responses in the skin. Contact allergies seen on the belly where little hair covers the skin are quite common in the dog. The problem, a real one, is to identify the offending substance. It may be dye in carpets, substances used for cleaning floors, bedding material, plants in the grass, the list is endless. If the substance causing the allergic response can be identified and removed then the condition will disappear. If not then a number of palliative treatments are used to reduce the distress of the dog. A generalised allergy which manifests itself in the skin is urticaria (also called nettle rash or hives). In this condition patches of skin swell up all over the body including the head. The condition seems particularly common in boxers, but is by no means restricted to them. This condition appears suddenly and usually regresses rapidly. Prevention depends again on identification of the causative substance – a task which in practice proves extremely difficult.

Nutritional skin problems

Diets deficient in important or essential food components can cause skin disease. With the generally high standards of dog nutrition found in the U.K. it is unlikely that a dog will be found to suffer from deficiency or imbalance of the diet. However, occasionally dogs are thought to have a low level of polyunsaturated fatty acids, which will cause a dry skin, scurf and a lifeless coat. The addition of a teaspoonful of corn oil or soft margarine will rectify the deficiency.

Miscellaneous skin conditions

Eczema

This term is very much misused in veterinary dermatology. It is not a specific condition. Very often owners are terrified of the word and express considerable disquiet if it is used. Wet or moist eczema is a term applied to one condition very sudden in onset.

Moist or wet eczema or dermatitis

This is a condition which occurs in all types of dog but which is more common in long haired breeds. It is characterised by the large patch of skin devoid of hair with a moist yellow discharge. The animal is depressed and sometimes has a high body temperature. Much of the condition is due to self inflicted damage by the dog. The cause of the condition remaining unknown although some authorities believe it to be due to a neuritis. It usually responds rapidly to treatment.

Alopecia

Alopecia means loss of hair. This is due to hormone problems.

Impetigo

A condition common in puppies characterised by pustules on the abdomen, on the inside of the legs and more rarely around the head. The condition is due to a bacterial infection which responds to antibiotics and medical washes of afflicted areas.

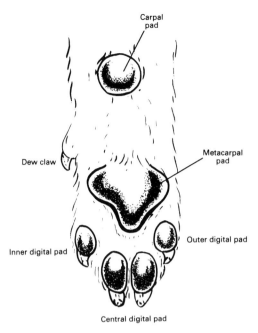

Dog's pad

Interdigital cysts

These appear as painful swellings between the toes. They are often very large and the skin appears stretched and shining. Interdigital cysts occur in all breeds but are quite common in the bull breeds and in cocker spaniels. The cause of the condition is unknown. Treatment consists of antibiotics and if persistent, autogenous vaccine – vaccine made by a laboratory specifically for the individual dog. In some cases the cysts are opened surgically and the lining destroyed by scraping. The condition presents a real problem in afflicted dogs since a permanent cure is unlikely.

Interdigital dermatitis

Dogs occasionally develop a severe, often moist, dermatitis between the toes and on the feet. It is probably caused by damage either of a physical or chemical nature, for example when the dog steps on a sharp object or some noxious substance. The condition is exacerbated by the dog's diligent or persistent use of the tongue. This condition responds well to treatment.

Paronychia

This condition starts as an infection of the nail bed – that area where the nail joins the skin. The condition if left untreated rapidly worsens, the toes swell, are hot and painful and the dog is lame. Paronychia responds well to local application of warm water, antibiotic cream and in severe cases tablets or injections of antibiotics.

Dermatitis

A word simply meaning inflammation of the skin.

Collie nose

A specific condition common in, but not exclusive to, rough and border collies and Shetland sheepdogs. The cause is unknown. The condition is gradual in onset, classically near the nose. The skin loses its pigment, becomes wet, may suppurate and cause irritation. Eye lesions may also be present. A very difficult condition to deal with effectively.

Moulting

Wild dogs and wolves moult twice a year. Many domestic dogs retain this pattern. There are however individuals in several breeds that seem to moult continuously. This problem causes considerable social difficulties in some households. While there may be a skin condition, which could be treated with advantage, most of the problems of this kind appear to have no solution. It is a canine cross to be borne.

Slipped disc

Slipped disc, more technically intervertebrate disc protrusion, is a common problem which afflicts some breeds of dog more than others. Slipped discs occur in two regions along the spinal cord either in the neck region (cervical discs) or in the middle of the back (thoraco-lumbar). When the neck discs are affected the animal is usually in acute pain, tries not to move, may stumble on all four legs and will often resist going up or down steps or stairs. In addition it may be reluctant to bend its head to its bowl to eat.

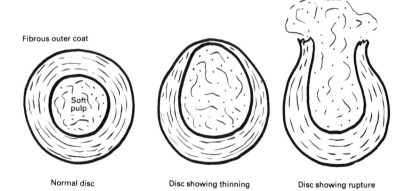

Fibrous outer coat

Soft pulp

Normal disc   Disc showing thinning   Disc showing rupture

Back discs often cause severe pain with reluctance to move. The dog emits sudden cries of pain, particularly when touched or lifted. Severely afflicted dogs may have faecal or urinary incontinence and in some cases paralysis of the hind quarters. In the latter situation the pain may disappear but the dog just drags itself along with hind legs trailing behind. The condition is serious.

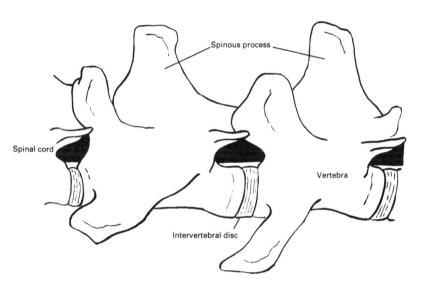

Actual position of disc

The intervertebral discs separate each bone (vertebrae) of the spine, acting as a soft cushion to prevent damage. (See diagram) Each disc is composed of a tough fibrous outer coat and a soft central pulp. For reasons not understood the fibrous outer coat sometimes thins. As this occurs the disc bulges at that point. If the thinning and bulging impinges on the spinal cord which runs above the disc then pain occurs. On occasions the disc actually bursts and the soft centre suddenly escapes into the vertebral canal causing considerable damage to the spinal cord, often resulting in paralysis. When the disc bursts, reminiscent of a balloon popping, the two vertebrae on either side are no longer separated effectively and they move closer together, a fact observable on X-ray examination. It is also sometimes possible to see discs whose structure is degenerating on X-ray.

The treatments for discs are legion. Essentially the veterinary surgeon's job is to treat the symptoms of pain, incontinence and paralysis while the nervous tissue of the spinal cord recovers from the damage caused by the pressure of the disc. Many cases can be successfully treated medically. Severe or recurrent cases may respond with surgery. Surgery aims at removing the pressure on the cord. The operation is far from easy and is not without serious risks, but often produces remarkably effective cures. Where permanent paralysis occurs euthanasia is sadly the best course although some owners prefer to put the dog's hind quarters on a set of wheels, the body being placed in a sling. This is possible in small breeds which often become very adept in their wheelchair, but has practical difficulties in larger breeds.

Dachshunds are, not surprisingly, most likely to be affected with disc problems but are closely followed by pekinese and cocker spaniels.

Spleen

The spleen is a complex organ with functions closely related to the production and maintenance of blood cells. It can be removed without any apparent effect because its functions can be taken over by other parts of the body. Splenectomy (removal of the spleen) may be necessary following a road accident in which it is ruptured or because it is afflicted with cancer.

Spondylitis

Describes an arthritic condition of the spine. Afflicted dogs show varying degrees of pain. There may be difficulty in climbing stairs, occasional lameness, reluctance to move and resistance when picked up. The condition is usually slow in onset although the symptoms may appear suddenly. The diagnosis is confirmed with X-ray examinations. Treatment, aimed at alleviating symptoms is similar to that used in other forms of arthritis. (See Arthritis)

Stomatitis

Inflammation of the mouth. Usually caused by damage from playing with sticks or twigs, but can also be a symptom of general disease. Dogs usually refuse food, appear depressed and may salivate profusely. They often have considerable difficulty in drinking.

Stroke

A stroke occurs when a clot forms in one of the blood vessels in the brain. Symptoms are variable but the dog usually falls to the ground in a 'fit'. It may breathe badly and paddle its feet. Recovery may be very slow. It may be unable to stand, appear not to know its owner and be depressed. Occasionally a drooping of one side of the face can be seen with a weakness of the leg on the same side. Some dogs walk in circles after a stroke.

The condition is commoner in old dogs being extremely rare under nine years of age. Most dogs either die at the time of the stroke or recover completely. There is rarely, if ever, the distressing symptoms of partial recovery and mental disability which is such a factor of human strokes. Treatment is well worth while. Recovery is common.

Tapeworms

Tapeworms are good parasites. That is to say efficient parasites. If one wants to be a parasite it is certainly not a good idea to kill your host and much better if you don't make him ill or even let him know you are present. All this most tapeworms of the dog achieve. After all, a little tapeworm sitting quietly in the gut will not take much of its host's food. It rarely causes any discomfort to the host and indeed the only way most owners know that their dog has a tapeworm is when they see segments appear as wriggling, moving rice grain-like objects near the anus or left where the dog has been sitting. Common tapeworms of the dog in Great Britain are of little importance to dogs and of no significance at all to the dog's owner save offending their aesthetic sensitivity.

Tapeworms are not passed from dog to dog directly but must pass through a second or intermediate host during their development. Depending on the type of tapeworm the eggs must be swallowed by the secondary host in which they hatch, pass through the larval stages and then sit waiting for a dog to eat them. Secondary hosts include fish, rabbits, sheep, rats and mice but the commonest tapeworm of the dog (dipylidium caninum) has as its recording host, the dog flea. Once inside the dog the head of the tapeworm attaches itself to the intestine wall and begins to grow. As each segment ripens, becoming full of eggs, it breaks from the rest of the worm and passes out of the anus to begin a new cycle.

Various drugs are used to remove the tapeworm from the gut. It is also important to try to prevent re-infection by keeping the dog free from fleas.

TEETH
Parodontal disease
The cause of this condition has been described. (See Symptoms, Bad teeth) The teeth are often presented to the veterinary surgeon in a very bad condition with thick layers of tartar, considerable quantities of pus and an extremely offensive smell. Treatment requires that the dog be given a general anaesthetic, the tartar removed and any loose teeth extracted. It is general to wash the gums with a mild antiseptic and in severe cases give antibiotics for a few days. Prevention is better than cure. Ask your veterinary surgeon to look at the teeth regularly and have them cleaned before they get to the stage of parodontal disease.

Retention of milk teeth
Some dogs, particularly the smaller breeds may not lose all of their milk teeth as the adult teeth erupt. The most commonly retained are the canine or eye teeth, the four long large teeth at the front of the mouth. If left in place they act as traps for food and predispose the dog to dental disease. They are very easily removed.

Distemper teeth
Some adult teeth erupt with pitted and brown-stained enamel. It is thought to be due to some general infection at the time the enamel is forming. Since infection in pups used to be commonly caused by distemper they are often so called. The condition is less frequent now that distemper is less common. The condition is unsightly but does not predispose dental disease.

Testicular tumours
A swollen testicle particularly in an old dog which is not painful is likely to be a tumour. Professional advice is essential. There are several kinds of testicular tumour, one – the Sentoli cell tumour – incredibly produces female hormones, which have the effect of causing feminisation of the dog. The dog shows swelling of the penile sheath, elongating nipples, loss of hair and may be attractive to other male dogs. It will often itself appear lethargic. In all cases of testicular tumour, the tumour should be removed surgically. Sexual abnormality usually regresses following excision.

Tetanus
This is a very rare condition in the dog. Dogs with tetanus have a characteristic look about the head. The ears appear erect and are pulled together, the skin between them is wrinkled. The dog may walk rather stiffly and may appear excitable. In some cases the third

Ask your veterinary surgeon to look at your dog's teeth regularly

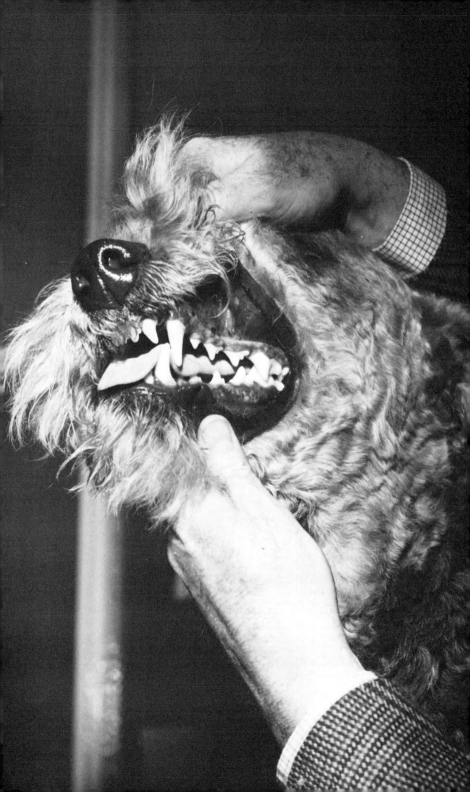

eyelid covers part of the eye. Swallowing and lapping may be difficult. The condition is often fatal.

Treatment depends on killing the bacteria which causes the condition with antibiotics, neutralising the effect of the toxin which produces the symptoms with antiserum and feeding those dogs which cannot swallow artificially. (See Part II, Vaccination)

Tonsillitis

Inflammation of the tonsils. Dogs with this condition may appear distressed, refuse food and show considerable reluctance or difficulty in drinking. There may be a tendency to salivate. Some dogs with tonsillitis gag or make choking or coughing movements and may bring up a frothy clear fluid. Affected dogs may have a raised temperature. Tonsillitis may be one factor in generalised disease. Kennel cough and distemper both show a tonsillitis as one manifestation of their presence. Tonsillectomy – the removal of tonsils – is rarely performed in the dog but may be indicated if the inflammation is persistent or recurrent. Malignant cancer of the tonsils is not uncommon in the dog.

Travel sickness

Dogs afflicted with travel sickness often become distressed soon after entering a car. They rapidly become anxious, begin to pant and often salivate profusely. Recently consumed food will be regurgitated to be followed by copious quantities of frothy mucus. The symptoms abate rapidly when the journey is completed. The condition can be controlled by the prudent use of medicines but since prevention is better than cure a programme of familiarisation is useful. (See Part I, Behavioural problems, and Part II, Travelling with dogs)

Tuberculosis

Fortunately this condition is now rare in the dog. Public health schemes to eradicate the disease in the human population have incidentally benefited the dog. Symptoms are insidious in onset. Owners often do not seek advice until the condition is well advanced. The symptoms vary but afflicted dogs are usually emaciated, have difficulty in breathing and may cough. Some cases show vomiting and diarrhoea.

Treatment is not advisable and could even be considered irresponsible because of the public health aspect.

Urolithiasis – stones in the bladder

The formation of stones in the urinary tract occurs in both male and female dogs. Unlike man, kidney stones are rare. Small bladder stones or sand occur in male dogs while bitches commonly have one or more very large stones. The symptoms are reminiscent of cystitis. Dogs tend to strain when passing water, may show thirst and sometimes blood in the urine, particularly noticeable after exercise when the stone may damage blood vessels in the bladder wall. Stones may be felt, but X-rays are often used to confirm their presence. Surgery, the opening of the bladder (cystomy), is the usual treatment. Unfortunately, the cause of stone formation is unknown but recent research has provided us with preventative procedures. The stones should therefore be analysed to identify the particular regime concerned.

The penis in the dog has a small bone surrounding the tube (urethra) which carries the urine from the bladder through the penis. This effectively prevents the passage of all but the smallest stones. The male therefore suffers from obstruction of the urethra, a condition from which the bitch is spared. The classic symptom is the frequent attempts of the dog to pass urine, with little or no success. This symptom is not exclusive to a blocked urethra, but the condition is so serious and prompt attention so imperative that professional advice must be sought without delay if the condition is suspected. Diagnosis is confirmed by passing a fine tube (catheter) up the urethra to identify a blockage. Treatment is surgical under general anaesthetic, an opening is made along the penis, just behind the bone and the stones removed. This opening is usually left open so that urine initially passes from the wound. After a few days the wound heals and urination returns to normal. Occasionally stones block the urethra before the small bone in the penis, in which case an opening may be made elsewhere. In rare cases where the blockage is repeated a permanent opening is made below the anus. This allows urine to flow in spite of the blockage at the small bone.

Vaginitis

Inflammation of the vagina. This condition is usually caused by infection gaining entry from outside. There is considerable irritation, the bitch licks the area and there is often a purulent discharge. The condition is quite common in young bitches. Apart from these local symptoms the bitch does not appear ill. Treatment depends on antibiotics, by injection or tablet and the application of antiseptic or antibiotic creams into the vagina.

Vulvitis

Inflammation of the vulva. The vulva may be inflamed together with the vagina. (See Vaginitis) There is also a very persistent ulcerative vulvitis and perivulvitis. This is often due to physical abnormalities of the vulva which cause the creases surrounding the vulva to become red raw and very sore. The bitch licks continually. These conditions are often difficult to cure. Local applications of antibiotic and anti-inflammatory creams may help and in some cases surgery can be employed.

Nursing

Nursing has long been recognised as an essential adjunct to successful medical and surgical treatment in man. Its value is no less essential in veterinary medicine. The purpose of nursing is to cater for the physical and mental needs of the patient until the condition for which the animal is being treated is resolved by the ministrations of the veterinary surgeon. Nursing is always carried out under the guidance of the attending veterinary surgeon who may issue detailed nursing instructions for a specific condition. Where those instructions differ from the general remarks made below they should always take precedence and must always be meticulously observed. Nursing should be aimed at alleviating as much pain, distress and discomfort as possible.

Bedding

Dogs are creatures which respond to comfort. Great care must be taken to ensure that a soft warm dry bed is available. Blankets are advisable and should be of the cellular variety, to prevent suffocation and for easy cleaning. The room should be kept warm without over-heating, well ventilated and of moderate humidity. It is pointless to perform complicated surgery or sophisticated medical therapy and then to put the patient in a damp shed on a bed of straw. Patients should be watched regularly and, if reluctant or unable to move, turned from side to side every hour to help prevent bed sores. When the bed becomes soiled with urine or faeces it should be changed. While most cats prefer to be away from people when they are ill, dogs often enjoy the presence of human company and in particular their owner. In most cases of illness some restriction of movement is advisable. A crude indoor cage can be created from fire guards or chairs.

Feeding

When we feel ill or are recovering from an operation we usually need a little coaxing to eat even the most appetising of food. We need our palate tickled. Dogs are like us. A large plate of tinned dog food or a dollop of meat and biscuit is not likely to tempt the delicate canine patient. Small amounts of steamed fish, scrambled egg or even milk puddings may well stimulate appetite. Small feeds frequently offered are more acceptable than the normal one meal a day routine. The dog should never be force fed, *but never*.

Drinking

Water should as a principle always be available but the very sick patient may be unable to reach water so it must be assisted. The dog's head should be raised and the bowl held in a convenient position for it to lap. Milk or milk and water may be offered if preferred. When the dog is so weak that it cannot lap, the mouth should be wiped very frequently with moist cotton wool. Indeed the latter can be moist enough to squeeze drops into the dog's mouth if it is able and willing to swallow. When fluid cannot be taken by mouth or when the dog is unable to imbibe then a fluid drip will be set up by the veterinary surgeon. Water should *never* be poured down a dog's throat.

Urination

House trained dogs suddenly placed indoors can present problems. Where possible dogs should be walked to enable them to relieve themselves. If this is not possible then gentle pressure on the abdomen will overcome the dog's natural inhibitions. Once started little will stop the flow save completion. In some cases catheterisation may be necessary and will be performed by the veterinary surgeon.

Defaecation

Horrific tales of nursing sisters instituting enematic rites for human patients who offered a negative answer to more than three discrete daily defaecatory enquiries are perhaps the least attractive legends of the nursing profession. In practice dogs are able to refrain from defaecation for several days without untoward effect. In nearly all cases defaecation recommences as soon as the stage of recovery is reached which allows gentle lead exercise. Enemas as a tool for the nursed patient are almost never required. They are reserved for genuine constipation or for rectal foreign bodies.

Grooming

Over zealous grooming is not indicated in the very ill patient. Sick dogs will not enjoy the ministrations of a hearty nurse vigorously applying bristle to hair. There is no doubt however that except in extremely ill, prostrate patients, a little gentle combing of long coated dogs probably improves comfort. As already mentioned under

Drinking the gums and teeth should be wiped with a moist piece of cotton wool. Indeed all orifices including the eyes and the nose should be cleaned of dirt and discharge.

Inhalants

Following closely the clearing of nasal discharge should come a simple inhalant of steam or Friars Balsam to relieve congested nasal chambers.

Nursing the surgical cases

Before a dog has an operation it is wise where possible to give the dog a bath. The advisability of bathing will obviously depend on whether or not it is an emergency operation and the state of general health of the dog.

Nursing animals to health after surgery is very important to the success of the operation. In some cases, where constant professional attention is essential, dogs may be kept by the veterinary surgeon and nursed by qualified staff. If the animal is to be nursed at home it is always a good idea to restrict the dog's movements for at least a few days. A simple indoor kennel or cage can be constructed by partitioning off a corner of the room with chairs, settees or nursery fire guards. The bed has already been described.

Movement puts tension on wounds and tends to pull the stitches. This is to be prevented at all costs. Dogs must not be taken for walks. It is amazing how many owners ignore one's advice and their own common sense to take quite ill dogs with large surgical wounds for walks to the park or common. After operations dogs should be kept quiet. They should not be allowed to run free in the house and must not jump on furniture or climb stairs. When going out for essential toilet evacuations they should be kept on a lead, even in the owner's garden. One sudden leap can do untold harm. Some wounds may be bandaged in which case advice on re-dressing will be given by the veterinary surgeon. In many cases wounds are left uncovered. Providing a reasonable degree of surgical skill has been employed to close the wound, most animals will leave the wound alone or at least show only limited interest in it. All attempts to lick or worry the wound must be admonished by the owner. Any wound that gives the slightest cause for concern to the owner should, indeed must, be returned to the veterinary surgeon for examination.

Handling

Good handlers have an empathy with their animals. They understand and develop a relationship with them which allows certain liberties to be taken. Much of this is gained by experience but a great deal can be learned, though it takes time. This small section can do no more than provide the materials.

Handling starts from a very early age ideally from soon after birth. Puppies must become accustomed to being examined. If they show reluctance to have an area of the body touched or looked at then each day the owner should, with resolution, examine the area. One of my own pups for example didn't like its feet touched. Each night for several weeks the feet were examined meticulously, in spite of verbal and physical resistance by the pup, until it accepted that it was my right to look at its feet when and how I liked. Always insist from the very beginning that you can handle any part of your pup without protest. Its life may one day depend on your ability to do so.

All dogs can be controlled, providing you have a collar and lead or slip noose around its neck. If further restraint is necessary then a bandage around the snout gives almost complete control. Make a loop of a length of bandage, by tying a simple knot but leaving it open. Place the loop around the dog's jaws. Pull the loop tight – you cannot obstruct its breathing – cross the bandage under the jaws and tie behind the ears using a bow for quick release. Pull it reasonably tight. If the dog resists the application of the tape, as some will, when they realise what you are about, it will be essential to have a confident assistant to hold the dog tight behind the ears. In extremely difficult cases, where you have to perform prescribed nursing techniques on a difficult dog, tranquillisers may be prescribed by your veterinary surgeon.

Administration of medicines

An important feature of nursing is the administration of medicines in one form or another.

Tablets are perhaps the commonest way of giving drugs. For the right handed nurse, the left hand should be placed across the top of the dog's upper jaw with the thumb towards you. The middle finger on the far side and the thumb on the side nearest the nurse should be pressed under the top lip and behind the large canine teeth. The right hand, holding the tablet between thumb and forefinger, should depress the lower jaw using the middle finger. The tablet can then be placed far to the back of the throat over the base of the tongue. Well back, the tablet stimulates the swallow reflex and an untimely return of the tablet is impossible. If the jaws are held almost but not quite shut, the tongue will appear between the front teeth and slide up to lick the nose. This indicates that the tablet has definitely been swallowed.

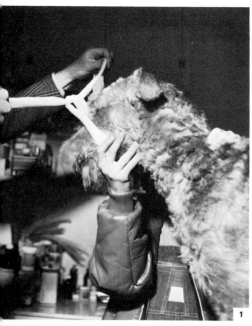

A tape over the snout ensures
complete control over a
snappy patient.
1 Loop tape over snout
2 Cross tape under jaw
3 Tie tape firmly behind ears

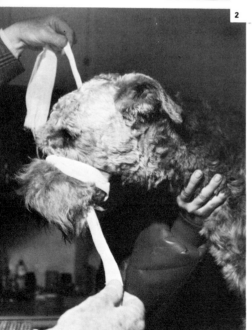

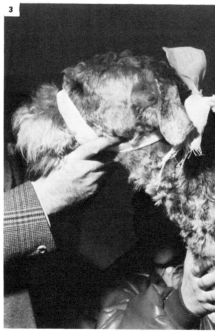

If a dog is very ill but struggles against this simple method, or if yellow bellied fear inhibits the owner, most tablets can be crushed into a powder and mixed with a little honey, syrup or jam and smeared on the teeth. The dog will be forced to lick it. If the dog is eating and if tablets are to be mixed in food it is best to crush the tablet, mix it with a small portion of the food and give that separately before the main meal. Some dogs will take tablets hidden in soft bars of chocolate.

Liquid medicines may be mixed in foods. Fastidious dogs sometimes refuse food so defiled presumably because of a strange smell. To administer liquids great care should be taken, particularly in sick dogs, that fluid is not poured accidentally down the trachea into the lungs. The head should be tilted very slightly upwards and with the teeth closed the lip at the corner of one side of the mouth pulled out to make a pouch. The liquid can be slowly poured into this pouch from a spoon, dropper or hypodermic syringe, the latter kindly supplied by the veterinary surgeon. The head should be held still tilted slightly upwards until the dog has swallowed the medicine.

Accidents

Two considerations are paramount when attending to a dog which has been involved in any kind of accident. First make sure you don't get hurt. Dogs are often extremely frightened following an accident, and may be in pain as well as in a state of shock. Secondly the patient must be handled as gently as your safety allows, making sure not to exacerbate its injuries. It is always a wise precaution to put a tape around the dog's jaws to prevent it biting before moving. Lift the dog carefully, put it on a soft bed, if possible, cover any wound with clean dry cotton sheet or surgical gauze and seek professional advice as soon as possible. Complicated first aid measures beyond those demanded by normal common sense usually do little but delay the intervention of veterinary attention.

Part Four

Deciding on euthanasia (mercy killing)

Everybody would like an old friend to live its life in health right up to the end, go to bed one night and simply not wake up. A marvellous way to go. Unfortunately there are many cases when it doesn't happen quite as pleasantly as one would wish. There comes a time when, after an illness or long period of decline, you are advised to have your dog destroyed, in its own interests. This can never be an easy decision. How does one decide? While there's life there's hope! As well recognised in the field of human euthanasia, there is no guarantee that every decision would be correct. Dog owners can do no more, and can be expected to do no more, then make, what appears to them at the time, the most reasonable decision based on current professional advice and on their own common sense. If the veterinary surgeon responsible for the case has explored every possible avenue of treatment without success, and if the dog is clearly distressed, apparently unhappy, or in pain with no reasonable hope of improvement or recovery, then it would be selfish of an owner to prolong the suffering.

That is not to say that every animal that becomes ill or suffers from a road accident should be destroyed rather than let it suffer. This attitude, much more prevalent among dog owners than veterinary surgeons, is frequently encountered. So long as there is a reasonable chance of recovery then treatment should continue. Veterinary surgeons are in the business of saving life not taking it.

Euthanasia

Once euthanasia has been decided upon it should be carried out quickly and efficiently, but above all with sympathy and understanding. Several methods have been used, but the one most commonly used is the administration of an overdose of barbiturate. A personal preference is to have the animal held by an experienced assistant with the owner at the dog's head to comfort it. The dog is then given an intravenous injection of barbiturate which simply causes the animal to go first into a deep sleep, to be very rapidly followed by death. In most cases the dog is dead before the injection is completed. The method is

Silvermere Haven pet cemetery, Cobham, Surrey.

simple, painless – apart from the needle prick – and if carried out with sympathy causes little distress to the dog.

Owners must decide if they can remain with the dog while euthanasia is carried out. For some, the experience would be too painful, too distressing. In that case elect to leave the dog in the competent hands of the veterinary surgeon, having established that euthanasia will be completed without delay.

Some owners prefer euthanasia to take place in the home. This is very understandable and most veterinary surgeons will agree.

Disposal of the body

This is always a very difficult subject and one which causes distress to the owner and concern to the veterinary surgeon who has to provide some kind of disposal service.

Perhaps the most satisfactory solution is for the owner to bury the dog in their own garden. Where this is not possible, disposal is left to the veterinary surgeon. In many parts of the country bodies are collected commercially. Fortunately there are now cremation services available and many owners find this a preferable alternative.

While there have always been a few pet cemeteries, the number has increased in recent years. For those who wish to demonstrate their affection for a dead companion by reverence for its mortal remains pet cemeteries offer a good service. Many offer a range of possibilities from simple communal burial, individual graves with or without headstones and cremation.

The Blue Cross Animals Hospital
1 Hugh Street
Victoria
London
SW1V 1QO
Tel: 01–834 5556

British Veterinary Association
7 Marsfield Street
London
W1M 0AT
Tel: 01–636 6541

Dog Breeders Insurance Co Ltd
27 Beacon House
Lansdowne
Bournemouth
BH1 3LE
Tel: 0202 293543

**Equine & Bloodstock Insurance Co
    Ltd**
Marlow House
610/616 Chiswick High Road
London
W4 5RU
Tel: 01–995 8331

The Kennel Club
1 Clarges Street
Piccadilly
London
W1Y 8AB
Tel: 01–493 6651

Ministry of Agriculture
State Veterinary Service
Hook Rise South
Tolworth
Surbiton
Surrey
KT6 7NF
Tel: 01–337 6611

National Canine Defence League
10 Seymour Street
Portman Square
London
W1H 5WB
Tel: 01–935 5511

P.D.S.A. (Head Office)
South Street
Dorking
Surrey
RH4 2LB
Tel: 0306 81691

Pet Plan Insurance
32 Wood Lane
London
W12 7DU
Tel: 01–743 1841

**Royal College of Veterinary
    Surgeons**
32 Belgrave Square
London
SW1X 8QP
Tel: 01–235 4971

R.S.P.C.A. (Head Office)
Causeway
Horsham
Sussex
Tel: Horsham 64181

Index

Note: Page references in **bold** indicate diagrams or photographs